The **Online** Career Portfolio

For each of the activities in this workbook there are also activities online [...] assessments, career matching, online research and much more. The co[...] will culminate in the creation of your own personal **Career Portfolio** whi[...] online from anywhere in the world to view, print or share.

Activities (Apps)
Comprehensive suite of essential activities covering the entire Senior Cycle Guidance Programme

Useful tools to complete your career and college research

Watch your Career Portfolio grow as you complete online activities and research

Save important events and deadlines to your Key Dates App

Live News and Events from Colleges

Improve your study performance by creating a personal Action Plan

Complete self-assessments that match you to careers and courses

Keep a record of your career and course favourites

View important school notices and messages from your school guidance department

Reach+ Online is iPad / Android PC / Mac Compatible

i

Title
Reach⁺ Student Workbook

978-0-9933359-0-7

Authors
Durrow Communications

Editor
Sean Carton

Design, Layout & Illustrations
Sean Carton, Jean Fernandez

Contributors
John Carton, Marius Fitzsimons, Eimear Sinnott
Bernadette Walsh, Clair Ryan, Gordon Weldon

Reach⁺ Advisory Group

Images
iStockphoto, Wikipedia, MorgueFile

©CareersPortal.ie

Produced, Published and Printed in Ireland by Durrow Communications Ltd.

Third Edition published 2021 by Durrow Communications Ltd.

Durrow Communications Ltd
College House,
71-73 Rock Road,
Blackrock, Co. Dublin
Tel: +353 1 4402314
e-mail: info@careersportal.ie

Contents

Career Awareness

Few of us think very far ahead about our lives. Nonetheless, it's worth noting that you are likely to be working for at least 40 to 50 years. That means you will probably be retiring from paid work around 2070!

What will the world be like then? How will your working career influence other aspects of your life? What preparations can you make to help you along your journey? Given that we rarely consider these questions, it's worthwhile giving the exercise that follows your full attention.

Exercise: Choosing a Career?

Circle true (T), not sure (?) or false (F) for the following questions. Discuss your answers in class.

1	Choosing a career is straightforward.	T ? F
2	My Guidance Counsellor is the best person to tell me which career to pick.	T ? F
3	I should choose a career from a 'Best Careers' list.	T ? F
4	Making a lot of money will make me happy.	T ? F
5	Once I choose a career, I'll be stuck with it for life.	T ? F
6	If my friends are happy choosing a particular occupation, chances are I will be too.	T ? F
7	I should choose my future 3rd level course / career according to what the people who know me best - my parents/guardians, expect me to do.	T ? F
8	I should choose a career based on the best course or college I can get into.	T ? F
9	Career tests can tell me exactly what is right for me.	T ? F
10	I should select careers from those that are highest paying.	T ? F
11	I don't need help from anyone in order to choose what I want.	T ? F
12	There is very little I can learn about an occupation without trying it out.	T ? F
13	If I change career, everything I have learnt will go to waste.	T ? F
14	There is one perfect career for me.	T ? F
15	It's best to decide when I'm older – something interesting is sure to come along.	T ? F
16	Choosing a career is something you do after school.	T ? F
17	Most people know what career they want before they leave school.	T ? F
18	I should choose a career based on the subjects I get the best results in.	T ? F
19	It is best to choose one career path now and stick to it.	T ? F
20	I don't think any career would suit me.	T ? F
21	You need to be a certain personality type for most careers.	T ? F
22	The college course I choose must lead me directly into my career choice.	T ? F

Exercise: Career Timelines

The truth is, your career journey has already started! Past experiences and choices made by you and your family have already nudged you towards or away from possible occupations. Your experiences and how you handled them have helped form your attitudes and skills – all of which will contribute towards what you are and what you hope to become.

In this exercise we will look over a typical person's life to see how their life developed. The people below were asked to mark some key things in their life on a timeline. They were then asked to draw a line to indicate the 'good' and 'bad' times in their life. During the good times, they were asked to keep the line above the centre scale. During stressful or unrewarding times, they were to draw beneath the scale. The height of the line indicates how good or bad times were.

Michelle's Life: *Illustration of her life showing the traumas, ups and downs, unsuccessful transitions and recovery points.*

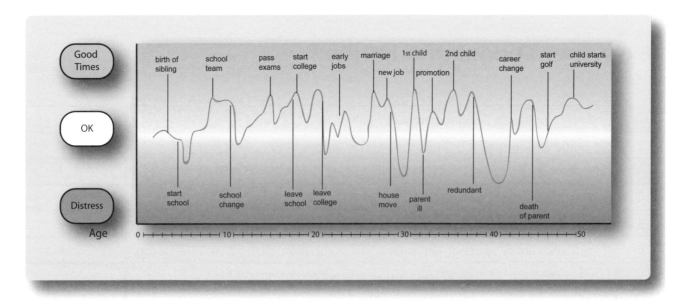

Now compare this lifeline with this next person, who has experienced different circumstances.

Ian's Life: *Illustration of his life showing the traumas, ups and downs, unsuccessful transitions and recovery points.*

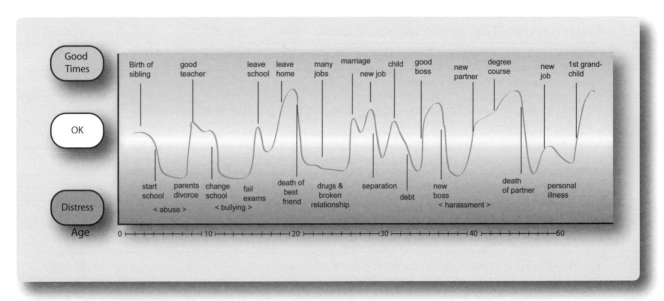

Ⓡ **Reach**⁺

Identify three events that marked **good times** during each person's life.	Identify three events that led to **sad or stressful** times.
Michelle's Life	**Michelle's Life**
1.	1.
2.	2.
3.	3.

Ian's Life	**Ian's Life**
1.	1.
2.	2.
3	3

Compare and contrast the lives of Michelle and Ian as revealed in their lifelines.

_____
_____
_____
_____
_____
_____
_____

One of the lives illustrated showed the person experienced more 'distress' in their life than the other. What factors other than the events themselves may have caused this to happen?

_____
_____
_____
_____
_____
_____
_____
_____
_____
_____

Michelle and Ian's lifelines covered their lives from birth right through to age 50 and beyond. In the next exercise, we ask you to fill in your lifeline from birth until now.

You might mention early memories of family, first day at school, membership of a club or team, memorable achievements, a sad time, school events, entering secondary school, junior cert, exam results, transition year, etc.

- First, recall some important events in your past. For each event, consider whether you remember it as 'a good time', a period of 'distress', or in-between. Place a marker on the timeline below to indicate the time when it happened and whether it was at a good time (top of graph), a period of distress (bottom of graph) or somewhere in-between.

- Secondly, draw a line from the first event up until now indicating how good or bad you think times have been during this period. Choose your own events.

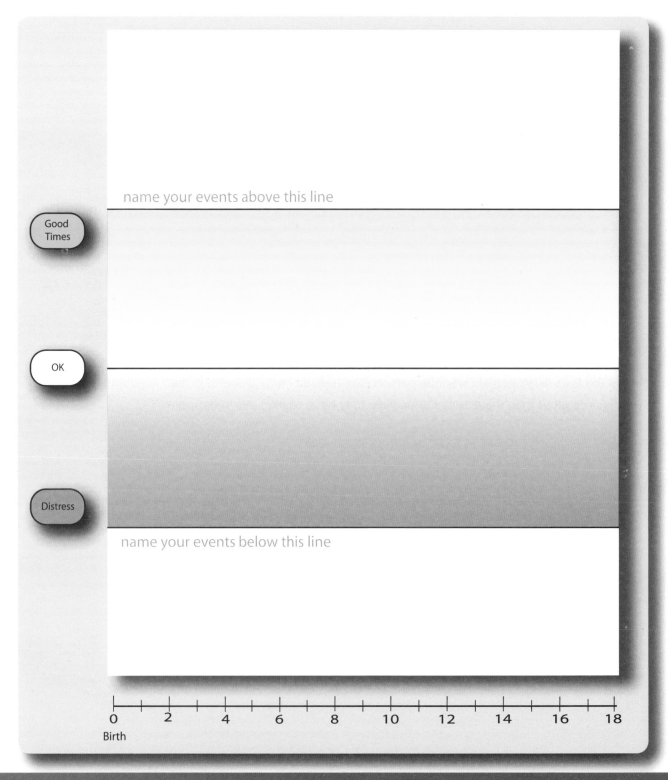

In the next diagram, we want you to imagine your future. Mark in some key events you think might happen in your life and how you might feel about them. You may use events chosen from Michelle or Ian's examples, but feel free to select your own.

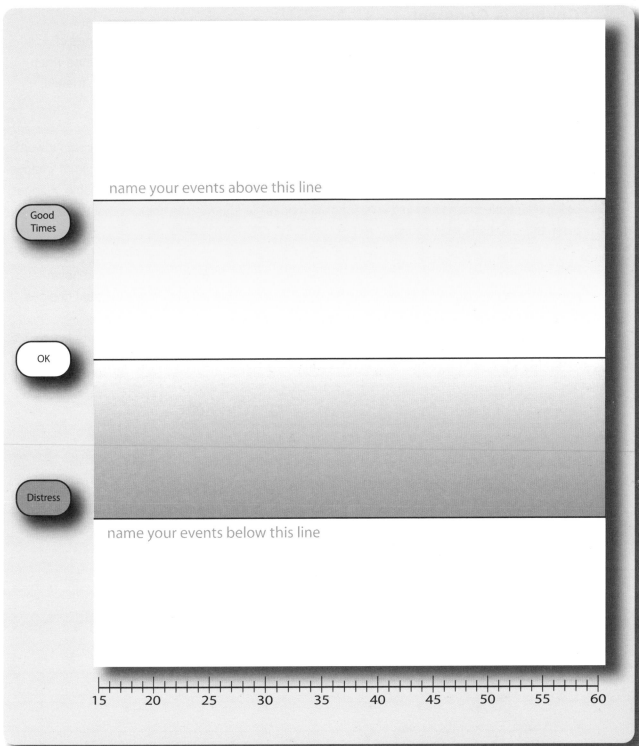

name your events above this line

Good Times

OK

Distress

name your events below this line

15   20   25   30   35   40   45   50   55   60

Exercise: The High Five Principles

Everybody experiences stress in their lives to varying degrees. While we all need certain levels of stress to help us perform to the best of our ability, too much stress and anxiety will have the opposite effect. The following guidelines provide a way of thinking which may help us to cope and deal with the pressures of life.

Career Guidance experts in Canada have come up with five simple but effective principles to help us prepare for what life will bring. The following exercise describes these 'High Five' principles and asks you to think about each one.

Can you find ways of making them work for you?

Change is Constant

Up until recent times, a job was a job for life. You, however, are likely to have a series of different jobs in a variety of occupational areas. Think about all the things that change when moving from one job to another: new job tasks, working colleagues, management, friends, salary, workplace, and possibly a new residence, to mention just a few.

By accepting that change is going to happen in your future, you are taking the first step towards addressing any stress or anxiety associated with that change. Applying this principle of 'change is constant' to your thinking means that you can be adaptable. In the face of inevitable change, being adaptable places you in the best position possible to make the choices most suited to you given the situations which arise.

When we are not adaptable to change, we are much more to likely to complain and have feelings of helplessness. When we feel this way, we are likely to fail to make suitable choices.

Recall one instance when something unexpected happened which caused a change in your life. How did you react to this change? [e.g. a birth or death in the family, moving house, loss of friend]

_____

_____

_____

_____

_____

_____

Would you react to it differently now?

_____

_____

_____

_____

_____

Reach⁺

Learning is Lifelong

A job may no longer be for life, but learning certainly should be. In order to handle the challenges that a changing world brings, it makes sense for us to keep updating our understanding of the world. Learning should not end with the Leaving Certificate, or even the completion of third level education. In order to keep up with the ever-changing fast paced working life of today, workers are required to regularly update their skills and knowledge.

What would you like to learn more about, aside from your Leaving Certificate subjects?

_____

_____

_____

_____

_____

_____

_____

_____

_____

_____

Focus on the Journey

Can you think of an event or incident when you learnt something new and unexpected about yourself? Perhaps a time when you left home, got involved in a new activity, or when you helped someone? [e.g. a school trip, work experience, personal incident etc...]

_____

_____

_____

_____

_____

_____

_____

_____

_____

Now consider this: life is a journey. Getting to know yourself will help reveal your goals and purpose and give you direction. However, people who are too fixed on a destination and too obsessed with the future can miss the doors of opportunity, relationships, situations and possibilities that present themselves along the way.

## Four

Seek Support

Imagine what life would be like without the support of others. We don`t often give our relationships the amount of thought they deserve. Other people's caring efforts can help reduce stress in our lives and contribute in lots of ways to help us reach our potential. It is important for us to be aware of who these people are, why they care, and the ways in which they help us.

Think about the various ways in which you offer support to others. This is a good starting point to help you appreciate how you can seek support from those around you.

Describe one way in which you are helpful to others and say why you give this support.

_____

_____

_____

_____

_____

_____

Name one important way in which another person helps you reach your potential and explain how they are helpful. [e.g. teacher, coach, friend, family member etc...]

_____

_____

_____

_____

_____

_____

In what ways do you think you will need support in the future? [e.g. advice, financial, confidence etc...]

_____

_____

_____

_____

_____

Who do you think are the people who will provide you with this support?

_____

_____

_____

## Five

Follow your Heart

As children we followed our heart without question. This freed us to imagine all sorts of possibilities which we then brought to our world of play. We dared to dream, and anything was possible. Because of this, we felt very alive and true to ourselves.

As we grow older it can be easy to lose sight of what our heart calls us to become. Our dreams can be threatened and even abandoned because of self doubts and pressures from others who distract us. However, the more effort we make to know ourselves, believe in ourselves and follow our heart, the stronger we become.

By taking a close-up look at our lives now, we may be lucky enough to find some clues to our dreams and discover what is most important to us. Following your heart often means having goals that seem bigger than who we are, yet at the same time we feel compelled to follow them.

Think of the many inventions and discoveries we would not enjoy in the world today if people had given up on their dreams. Although following your heart does not necessarily lead to fame and recognition, it is vital to choose the path to our dreams in order to enjoy a meaningful, purposeful and rewarding career. People who strive to discover this fifth principle of 'following their heart' are noted for their high levels of persistence, motivation and energy.

Give an example of an important personal event or experience in which you felt unusually strong and motivated. What did this experience reveal to you about yourself?

[e.g. sport / school achievement, doing your hobby, standing up for your beliefs etc...]

_____

_____

_____

_____

_____

_____

_____

_____

_____

_____

_____

_____

_____

_____

_____

Exercise derived from work produced by the National Life/Work Centre, Canada

Dreams and Ambitions

What do you want to be when you grow up?

No doubt you've been asked this question at some stage in your life. As a young child, you may have had a clear answer. As you grew older you probably changed your mind a number of times. As the years passed you have learned more about the world – and yourself – and so the direction and possibilities you see for yourself have also changed and developed.

Our childhood dreams can provide some interesting clues about our future choices. For some, they act like a compass – steering us in a particular direction over the course of our lives. For others they may simply hint at something that you admired, or valued.

Reflecting on your childhood aspirations, when you weren't afraid to dream and the world was full of possibilities, is a good starting point to finding a personal direction.

Past Dreams

All of us have had grand ideas at some point in our lives about what we would like to do when we grew up. Early ideas are often driven by being famous or heroic. Below is a mind map that one young person created that shows their dreams at various stages of their lives.

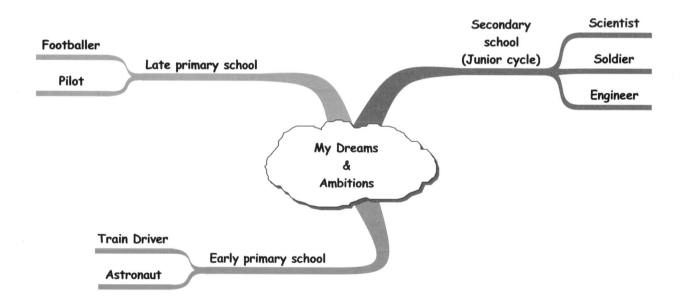

Exercise: My Past Dreams

+ | add to **Career Portfolio**

Fill in the mind map below with the dreams and ambitions you had during your past.

My Dreams
&
Ambitions

Exercise: My Current Dreams

Regardless of qualifications, talents, aptitudes or abilities needed, what would your dream job(s) be now?

Current Dreams

Role Models

Some people do things that seem remarkable and extraordinary. They seem to go beyond what we would expect ordinary people to be capable of. We can't help but notice them. We want to learn something from them – they have, after all, that 'magic' ingredient that sets them apart from the rest. Their remarkable actions also inspire us – they touch something inside us.

What we notice, what we give attention to, reveals something about ourselves. Focusing on the thoughts and feelings we have about remarkable people and their actions can help us find a direction in our personal journey that will satisfy and fulfill us.

When we are inspired by a person's action they often become role models for us. We imagine ourselves as having some of their qualities, and aspire to be a bit like them. Many young people are inspired by famous sportspeople, musicians, singers, actors and others in the public eye as their role models. Others will be inspired by experts working as engineers, teachers, doctors, lawyers, builders, accountants and so on.

We can also be inspired by the so called 'ordinary'. A young girl may look up to a 'stay at home mom' as a role model because that's what she aspires to be. Another girl may consider the president of her country as her role model as she is drawn to a future career that calls for leadership and responsibility. Similarly, a young man may see his father as his role model as he considers his father to be the kind of father that he wants to be in the future.

Ways to Inspire

The idea that we may be able to inspire others seems strange to most of us. We tend not to think that anything we do could be seen by others as inspiring. However, those who do inspire us rarely set out to do so. They simply follow their heart and do what they feel they must, but with more effort than most of us. Could it be that just making the effort makes the difference?

Exercise: Inspiring Ways of Being

Here are 10 great ways to inspire others by simply living life fully. Read through each of the points and score yourself on how well you generally do for each in your day-to-day life.

1. Be authentic and true to yourself.

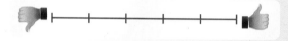

In this crazy world that's trying to make you like everyone else, find the courage to keep being your awesome self. Embrace that individual inside you that has ideas, strengths and beauty like no one else. Be the person you know yourself to be – the best version of you – on your terms. Above all, be true to **you**. No, it won't always be easy, because when it comes to living as a compassionate, non-judgmental human being, the only challenge greater than learning to walk a mile in someone else's shoes, is learning to walk a lifetime, comfortably, in your own.

2. Stick with what you love.

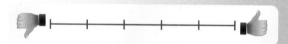

Take part in something you believe in. This could be anything. Some people take an active role in their local community, some find refuge in religious faith, some join social clubs supporting causes they believe in, and others find passion in their work or study. In each case the psychological outcome is the same. They engage themselves in something they strongly believe in. This engagement brings happiness and meaning into their lives. It's hard not to be inspired by someone who is passionate about what they're doing!

3. Express your enthusiasm.

Passion is something you must be willing to express if you want to inspire others. You can gain a lot of influence just by publicly expressing that you are excited and passionate about a topic. Expressive passion is contagious because of the curiosity it stirs in others. You'll get people wondering why you love what you love so much. Naturally, some of them will take the time necessary to understand what it is about the topic that moves you.

4. Excel at what you do.

People watch what you do more than they listen to what you say. Most people are inspired by GREAT musicians, writers, painters, speakers, entrepreneurs, engineers, mothers, fathers, athletes, etc. There's only one thing they all have in common: they excel at what they do. There's no point in doing something if you are not going to do it right. Excel at your work and excel at your hobbies. Develop a reputation for yourself, a reputation for consistent excellence.

5. Focus on building your character.

Be more concerned with your character than your reputation. Your character is what you really are, while  your reputation is merely what others temporarily think you are. A genuinely good character always shines and inspires in the long run.

6. Challenge people to do their best.

As Ralph Waldo Emerson once said, "Our chief want is someone who will inspire us to be what we know we  could be". If people know we expect great things from them, they will often go to great lengths to live up to our expectations.

7. Lead by example.

Practice what you preach or don't preach at all. Walk the talk! Be the change you want to see in the world. If you  really want to inspire others to do something, then this something should be a big part of your life. You don't necessarily need to be an expert at it, but you do need to be passionately involved.

8. Express what everyone else is thinking.

We are very connected to each other in various ways, the most important of which is our thoughts. Out of fear,  or passive shyness, lots of people hesitate to express their thoughts. If you take the risk and say the things others are holding back, you become the glue that brings people together.

9. Make people feel good about themselves.

People will rarely remember what you did, but they will often remember how you made them feel. Start noticing  what you like about others and tell them. Go out of your way to personally acknowledge and complement the people who have gone out of their way to excel. As von Goethe once said, "Treat a man as he appears to be, and you make him worse. But treat a man as if he already were what he potentially could be, and you make him what he should be."

10. Help people heal.

Instead of judging people by their past, stand by them and help repair their future. In life, you get what you put  in. When you make a positive impact in someone else's life, you also make a positive impact in your own life. Do something that's greater than you, something that helps someone else to be happy or to suffer less. Everyone values the gift of unexpected assistance and those who offer it.

Which ways of being characterise you most?

1. _____

2. _____

3. _____

Exercise: Who Inspires Me

> " *For anything great and good that you want to do in your life, there is one crucial prerequisite:* **inspiration.** *A good inspiration brings with it a wave of energy that by itself can propel you over the finish line. Conversely, when we are devoid of inspiration, everything can seem difficult, tedious and boring, and we get no joy out of what we are doing.* "
>
> Sri Chinmoy

In the following exercise we ask you to pick two people who inspire you and write down what it is you admire about them. They can be someone you know, or someone you just know about, such as a character from a book you have read, a film, a sports person, from history etc.

Who: _____

What this person does: _____

_____

What I find inspiring about this person: _____

_____

_____

Who: _____

What this person does: _____

_____

What I find inspiring about this person: _____

_____

_____

Who do you inspire?

Have you considered that what you do might inspire others? Have you ever noticed something you did which helped or influenced others? Write down any examples you can think of.

_____

_____

_____

_____

_____

Dream your future

| + | add to **Career Portfolio** |

Imagine yourself in 20–30 years from now having achieved something remarkable. What would you like to have done or achieved?

_____

_____

_____

Exercise: Carpe Diem

In the film **Dead Poets Society**, Robin Williams, who plays the part of a teacher, takes his English class out of their classroom, into the corridor. There he invites them to view the photographs of past pupils that hang on the walls and who are all long since deceased. He requests one of his students to read from the works of the 17th century poet Robert Herrick. The student, in a hesitant manner, slowly begins to read:

Gather ye rosebuds while ye may,
Old time is still a–flying,
And this same flower that smiles today,
To-morrow will be dying,

He goes on to explain that the same sentiment is expressed by the Latin phrase, Carpe Diem – meaning **seize the day**. "*Gather ye rosebuds while ye may. We are food for worms lads. Believe it or not, each one of us in this room is going to stop breathing and die.*"

He continues: "*I'd like ye to step forward over here and peruse the faces from the past. You've walked past them many times but I don't think that you have really looked at them. They are not that different from you, are they? Same haircuts, full of hormones, just like you. Invincible, just like you feel. The world is their oyster. They believe that they are destined to great things, like many of you. Their eyes are full of hope, just like yours.*"

"*But did they wait until it was too late to make their lives just one iota of what they were capable of? These boys are now fertilising daffodils.*" He then invites the boys to lean in and listen really hard to what their legacy is.

He then whispers '*Carpe Diem – seize the day. Make your lives extraordinary*'

Robin Williams passed away on Aug 11th 2014 - may he rest in peace.

What message do you think the teacher is trying to get across to his students?

_____

_____

_____

_____

Exercise: My Talents

+ | add to **Career Portfolio**

The following exercise draws attention to your natural talents and abilities. Expressing and appreciating them will help uncover where your strengths are as well as what dreams and aspirations you might harbour. Take your time and be relaxed and uncritical as you work through these sentences.

I get praised for...

_____

_____

I'm interested in...

_____

_____

If I had a great deal of money I would...

_____

_____

I would like to become an expert in...

_____

_____

I would like to be the kind of person who...

_____

_____

The most enjoyable thing I have ever done was...

_____

_____

I get a feeling of being worthwhile when...

_____

_____

Others say that I am...

_____

_____

I think I am good at...

_____

_____

> Considering what you have written above, what talents might you have?
>
> _____
>
> _____
>
> _____

Exercise: Find what you love

"I was lucky — I found what I loved to do early in life. Woz and I started Apple in my parents garage when I was 20. We worked hard, and in 10 years Apple had grown from just the two of us in a garage into a $2 billion company with over 4000 employees. We had just released our finest creation — the Macintosh — a year earlier, and I had just turned 30. And then I got fired.

How can you get fired from a company you started? Well, as Apple grew we hired someone who I thought was very talented to run the company with me, and for the first year or so things went well. But then our visions of the future began to diverge and eventually we had a falling out. When we did, our Board of Directors sided with him. So at 30 I was out. And very publicly out. What had been the focus of my entire adult life was gone, and it was devastating.

I really didn't know what to do for a few months. I felt that I had let the previous generation of entrepreneurs down - that I had dropped the baton as it was being passed to me. I met with David Packard and Bob Noyce and tried to apologize for screwing up so badly. I was a very public failure, and I even thought about running away from the valley.

But something slowly began to dawn on me — I still loved what I did. The turn of events at Apple had not changed that one bit. I had been rejected, but I was still in love. And so I decided to start over.

I didn't see it then, but it turned out that getting fired from Apple was the best thing that could have ever happened to me. The heaviness of being successful was replaced by the lightness of being a beginner again, less sure about everything. It freed me to enter one of the most creative periods of my life.

During the next five years, I started a company named NeXT, another company named Pixar, and fell in love with an amazing woman who would become my wife. Pixar went on to create the worlds first computer animated feature film, Toy Story, and is now the most successful animation studio in the world.

In a remarkable turn of events, Apple bought NeXT, I returned to Apple, and the technology we developed at NeXT is at the heart of Apple's current renaissance. And Laurene and I have a wonderful family together.
I'm pretty sure none of this would have happened if I hadn't been fired from Apple. It was awful tasting medicine, but I guess the patient needed it. Sometimes life hits you in the head with a brick.

Don't lose faith. I'm convinced that the only thing that kept me going was that I loved what I did. You've got to find what you love.

And that is as true for your work as it is for your lovers. Your work is going to fill a large part of your life, and the only way to be truly satisfied is to do what you believe is great work.

And the only way to do great work is to love what you do. If you haven't found it yet, keep looking. Don't settle. As with all matters of the heart, you'll know when you find it. And, like any great relationship, it just gets better and better as the years roll on. So keep looking until you find it. Don't settle.

This text is part of the Commencement address by Steve Jobs, CEO of Apple Computer and Pixar Animation Studios, delivered on June 12, 2005 to students of Stanford University, USA. A video of the full address is in your Career File on www.careersportal.ie Steve Jobs passed away on Oct 5th 2011 - may he rest in peace.

What do you think is remarkable about Steve Jobs' life?

_____

_____

_____

_____

What advice does he give to the students he is addressing?

_____

_____

_____

_____

Career Research

Why do Research?

Research refers to the work involved in finding out about something. It should involve getting information from a number of different sources, so that you can get a more complete understanding of whatever it is that is being researched.

For example, if you were to research what mobile phone to buy, you would probably read the specifications mentioned by the manufacturer. But you might also get useful information if you spoke to someone who already uses the phone. Or you might find a video on YouTube by an experienced reviewer who can tell you about their experience with it.

The more you research, the more your understanding develops. Mobile phones can be expensive, so doing research is a good idea if you want to get good value for your investment, and not be disappointed. Career research is similar. It's about combining information from a number of different sources to ensure you get a good understanding of what is involved in pursuing a particular career path. As with mobile phones, you may have to check out quite a few before you settle on one you like.

What you already know about many careers comes from people you've talked to, TV, films, books and other media. This is a good start, but the media is well known for misrepresenting reality. To find a more realistic view of individual careers and the educational requirements for them, you will need to do some personal research.

In the following three exercises, you will be asked to conduct research on **jobs**, **college courses** and **companies** in your area. It doesn't matter if you aren't interested in the specifics; the goal is to teach you what to look for and how to find it.

Exercise: What is that job really like?

1. Go to **www.careersportal.ie** and Log In.

2. Open **World of Work** tab and select the Career Explorer Tool from your **Reach⁺** Career File.

3. Using the Career Title filter, type in one of the following:

Farmer	Nurse	Engineer	Teacher

4. From the search results, choose one of the following occupation titles:

Farmer – Dairy	Nurse – Intellectual Disability	Engineer – Software	Teacher – Primary School

5. Preview details of the occupation using the ♥ button. Summarise what it says about this job:

_____

_____

_____

_____

6 Click on the **Career Title** to go to the details page. Select **The Work** tab and describe two tasks undertaken by this job:

_____

_____

_____

_____

_____

_____

7 Read through the various sections on the page. Use this information to describe what personal skills and qualities you think are required for the job in the section below:

_____

_____

_____

_____

_____

_____

_____

_____

_____

8 Occupations are often classified according to the level of education or experience required to fulfill the role. Occupations on CareersPortal are divided into 5 career **Zones**. What Zone is this occupation classified as and give an example of the typical education required to work in this job:

_____

_____

_____

_____

_____

_____

_____

9 Scroll down the page to view **Related Courses** for this job. Swipe through the list and select two courses that provide qualifications related to this career:

Course Code:	Course Title:	College:

10 Look through the page for links to related Videos and Interviews. Follow one link to either a **Video** or **Interview**. From that page, scroll to the panel that says **Ask me a question**. Choose questions about **Education and Training**. Enter the following:

Job holders name: _____   Occupation: _____

Did the person choose subjects in their Leaving Cert that helped them in their job?

_____

_____

_____

_____

11 Read the rest of the interview and describe one thing you learned about the job that was unexpected or particularly interesting:

_____

_____

_____

_____

_____

_____

12 Go back to the occupation page (click on 'Back' or use the browsers Back button). Find the **Job Search** section, and click on one of the popular Irish jobsites to search for jobs that are being advertised today that are related to the occupation. Find the nearest match for the occupation you are researching from the list and answer the following questions:

> **Note:**
> • You may have to try more than one link to find a job.
> • Some sites may use poor job filters, and may show unrelated jobs.

What is the **Job Title** for the job you selected?

_____

Identify two **skills** they're looking for: _____

_____

What **qualifications** or previous experience do they require? _____

_____

If no jobs for this occupation can be found, why do you think this might be the case? _____

_____

_____

Course Research

For most students, the biggest career choice they make during school is selecting a college course to take when they leave. Choosing a course is competitive, there are more students looking for places in college than there are places, and getting the course you want is not always easy.

Unfortunately, every year many students (over 10,000 students!) take up a course offer and soon find it is not what they like or expected. For many of these students they did not research what the course was about and had unrealistic expectations about what they were to study.

Knowing how to research courses is essential for most students. Course names alone do not provide enough information to justify committing your valuable time and money. Fortunately, Irish colleges provide plenty of information from which you can research the content of their courses.

Exercise: Will that course suit me?

1. Go to **www.careersportal.ie** and login

2. Open the **World of Education** tab and select the **CourseFinder Tool** from your **Reach⁺** Career File.

   In the filter panel, deselect any Career Interests that may be ticked. Then, use the **Career Sectors** filter to select the **Business Management & Human Resources** sector. Based on the results, answer the following:

   How many courses are found? _____

   Write down the title and college for one Level 6 Course: _____

   _____

   Preview details of the course using the ❤ button. Summarise what it says about this course from the Course Overview provided: _____

   _____

   _____

   _____

   _____

4. We are going to look for a business course in University College Cork (UCC). As there are so many courses and we only want courses in UCC, narrow your search results by using the **Colleges** filter to select UCC.

   How many courses are found? _____

   Name the course with the most Points (Tip - use the 'Sort by' filter) _____

   _____

   _____

   _____

5 Select CK203 Business Information Systems by clicking on the course title. Take note of the different items on this page and read the **Course Summary**. We will need more information than this to decide whether the course is suitable, so we will look for further information. Locate the **College Link** section and click on the college link to the course (opens in a new tab or window).

From the college page, find the following information:

How long does the course last? _____

What qualification will you be awarded? _____

What type of careers might this course lead you towards? _____

_____

_____

_____

6 Read through the course description and write down two facts about the course:

Fact #1: _____

_____

Fact #2: _____

_____

7 Look for information about the subjects (also known as modules) taught during the course. Often there is information about the modules for each year of the programme. Many courses offer both **core** and **elective** modules (core = must take, elective = usually some choice). Look through the information provided for this course and answer the following:

Name two core modules taken in first year:

_____

_____

Name one elective module taken in second year:

_____

> **Note:**
> • When researching a course you are genuinely considering, make sure you are interested in most of the modules on offer.

8 We want to find more details on some of the modules being offered. Look for details of individual modules on the page, or for a link to where such details can be found.

For one module, write down the following:

Module name: _____

Brief Description: _____

Number of Credits for this module: _____

9 Close the UCC tab / page to return to the CareersPortal course page. Check that you are back on the CareersPortal page for course CK203, and find the most recent points required for this course and enter them below:

Points: _____

Points can change every year. Select the **Entry Requirements** tab to view how points change from year to year – do the trends for this course suggest an increase or decrease for next year?

_____

10 From the section on **Entry Requirements**, answer the following:

How many subjects need to be taken at higher level? _____

Do you need a third language? _____

Do you need a science subject? _____

11 Next, find the section on **Related Courses**. This lists other courses in the general subject area from the same region. List one course from Munster Technological University (MTU), and one other course from any other college that looks similar to the course you are researching (i.e. combines business and computers). Fill in the details below.

> **Note:**
> • You will have to click on your chosen titles to get some of the information required.

	CAO Code:	Title	NFQ Level	Years	Points
From MTU:					
Other College:					

Congratulations. You are now ready to do the necessary research for courses that interest you.

Everywhere you go you will find people who are employed. As many people would prefer to be employed close to where they live, it is worthwhile knowing what employers are operating in your area. You might be surprised at the variety that exist, and the opportunities they may have to offer in the future.

Exercise - Company Research

Part 1

You have begun to think about working in your own locality, and wish to become more familiar with businesses that operate in your area.

Using the form below as a guide, research 6 local businesses and find the following information:

Name	#1	#2	#3	#4	#5	#6
Career Sector* Choose 6 different sectors						
Nature of Business						
How many employed						
How long operating						
Trade Internationally?						
Owner / Who started the business						

* A list of Career Sectors can be found on pages 176 - 177

For one of the businesses chosen, research the answers to the following questions:

What locations does the organisation operate from?

_____

_____

_____

_____

What are the main occupation types employed? _____

_____

_____

_____

_____

_____

_____

What are the main products or services offered by the organisation? _____

_____

_____

_____

_____

_____

_____

How does the organisation advertise and market its products/services? Does it have a website?

_____

_____

_____

_____

_____

What areas of the business/service are expanding and contracting? _____

_____

_____

_____

_____

_____

What occupations will the organisation most likely recruit for in the coming years? _____

_____

_____

_____

_____

Who are the main competitors? _____

_____

_____

How did the organisation start?
　　　　[Was there a single entrepreneur (name), what were the origins, what needs/problems were met?]

_____

_____

_____

_____

_____

_____

_____

_____

Who owns the organisation now? _____

_____

_____

_____

How does the company recruit new employees? _____

_____

_____

_____

Does the company offer work experience opportunities for school students? _____

_____

_____

Reach+

Every week in Ireland approximately 500 new businesses are started. Starting your own business can be an exciting and rewarding career opportunity, and usually benefits both the entrepreneur who takes the initiative, and the local community where the business is located. New companies can get assistance in setting up and managing their businesses by using a range of supports offered by Government agencies and private companies.

If you decided to setup your own business, what supports would you be able to receive in your own locality? Use the internet to research and answer the following questions. It may help to search online for "start your own business".

1   List three forms of support locally and outline how they could support you:

	Name of Organisation:	Services Offered:
#1.		
#2.		
#3.		

2   What is the web address (or phone number) of your local enterprise board: _____

_____

3   Have you ever considered starting your own business? Give a reason for your answer: _____

_____

_____

_____

_____

_____

_____

_____

_____

_____

_____

_____

_____

_____

_____

_____

Careers Fair

Careers fairs provide an opportunity for students to interact with staff from a large number of colleges, organisations and employers in a single day, or in the case of Virtual Fairs, over several days. Often this will be the first (and only) time you will get to engage with them, so it is an excellent opportunity to conduct some research.

Preparation:

Careers fairs are designed for the student. All the exhibitors are there to answer your questions and encourage you to apply to them when you leave school. They will have copies of their prospectus, application forms, leaflets and freebies (pens, highlighters, etc.). It's very easy to visit all the stands, collect as much as you can carry and learn absolutely nothing!

With a little preparation, you can do all that and learn something as well. Completing the **Careers Fair Planner and Checklist** before you go will give you a guide to follow once you're there. As you can see on the next page there are sections where you can fill in subject areas and courses which are of interest to you, so you won't forget what you're supposed to be researching.

Tips to help you make the most of a Careers Fair:

» Most careers fairs will organise some presentations on various relevant topics, some of which might interest you. Be sure to check the events schedule to make sure you don't miss them.

» Careers fairs are one of your only opportunities to meet with colleges outside Ireland, so make a point of visiting as many of them as possible. They might have courses which you hadn't previously considered, so be sure to talk with the exhibitor and pick up a prospectus if you're interested.

» It can be useful to ask the same questions to different colleges, as this helps you to compare them and their courses directly. You may also find students from the course you're considering, so speak to them about their experience.

» Students have a reputation for asking vague and confusing questions when inquiring about a course. If you arrive prepared, you can find out information which is relevant to you instead of the exhibitors general introduction.

> You can download additional copies of the Careers Fair Planner and Checklist sheet from the Careers Fairs App in the **Career Planning and Research** tab of your **Reach+** Career File.
>
> Note: This form has been designed to be folded into envelope size to make it easy to bring with you on the day.

Exercise: Careers Fair Planner and Checklist

Subject Areas of Interest:
- ☐ _____
- ☐ _____
- ☐ _____
- ☐ _____
- ☐ _____

Courses of Interest:
- ☐ _____
- ☐ _____
- ☐ _____
- ☐ _____
- ☐ _____

Presentations:

	NAME:	TIME:
☐		
☐		
☐		
☐		

Employment of Interest:
- ☐ _____
- ☐ _____
- ☐ _____

Courses found on the day:
_____
_____
_____

Finish at:
Time: _____
Location: _____
Supervisor's Ph. Number: _____

College Course Prompts:

Which courses do you have in this area?

How do these courses differ from one another?

What facilities do you have, and how do they compare with other colleges?

What links with industry do you have?

Can I benefit from any grants?

How many hours of lectures/tutorials/practicals will I have each week?

How big are the class sizes for lectures/tutorials?

Will there be any work placements as part of this course?

What kind of careers does this course lead to?

Do you have any advice in relation to this course?

What are the entry requirements for this course?

How do I apply for this course?

Are there fees for this course? When do I need to pay them?

Do many international students attend your college?

If I don't like the course, can I switch to a related programme?

My Questions:
_____
_____
_____
_____
_____
_____
_____

Questions for employers:
_____
_____
_____

Questions about Higher and Further Education:
_____
_____
_____
_____

Questions about International Study and Travel:
_____
_____
_____
_____

Questions about Studying Abroad:
_____
_____

Important Contact Details:
_____
_____

Number of Pens Collected: _____

Exercise: Exhibition Visit Report

Exhibition Name: _____

Date of Visit: _____

List any courses/colleges/training opportunities you are attracted to and why: _____

_____

_____

_____

List any courses/colleges/training opportunities you are no longer attracted to and why: _____

_____

_____

_____

What further information do you need to confirm your choices? _____

_____

_____

_____

Did you have a direct one-to-one conversation with anyone at the exhibition? Briefly note the details of

that conversation and any contact details. _____

_____

_____

_____

_____

How has your visit informed your choice of courses? _____

_____

_____

_____

Additional printable copies are available at www.careersportal.ie

College Open Days – Third Level

College open days are designed to introduce you to the exciting world of college life. They are run at great effort and expense by the colleges to encourage you to select a course with them. They are there to show you the college, the facilities they offer, and give you the opportunity to meet with their students, staff and lecturers. Some colleges run Open Days online - check the Open Days App for times and dates!

Where to find information on open days?
- In the **College Open Days App** in the **Career Planning and Research** tab of your **Reach⁺** Career File.

NOTE: You can save Career Events you are interested in onto your **Key Dates** App

Why Bother?

Apart from getting the day off school, there are a few great reasons to visit a college:

- Deciding on a course can be difficult, and colleges are full of people who are enthusiastic about what they study! If you're looking for direction, be sure to discuss your interests with as many people as possible.

- If you have chosen a subject area, next up is deciding where to study it. Open days are your single most valuable opportunity to compare everything about the colleges you're considering, from the lecturers and course facilities to the social life and how difficult it is to get there in the morning!

- A prospectus is no comparison to actually talking with your future lecturers and the current students. If you do end up in college, you will be there for at least two years, and often four or more, so you need to feel comfortable with your choice.

Semesters, Modules, Credits?

» Most third level colleges now structure their courses based on international standards. Each year of a course is split into two **semesters** of around 15 weeks each, the first from September to December/January, and the second continuing until May/June.

» During each semester, students usually take six **modules**, which are like miniature courses covering a certain area of knowledge. For example, a student studying English might take two Poetry modules, a module covering Shakespeare, a creative writing module, and two others.

» Modules can be **assessed** in a variety of ways. Most have an end-of-semester written examination, and many use continuous assessment (where written assignments, class tests, and practical work count towards the final grade).

» Passing a module earns 5 **credits**, which are a part of the European Credit Transfer (ECT) System. This system means that if you switch to another participating European college, the new college will be easily able to acknowledge your work to date.

Exercise: Talking the Talk

As the college system is different from school, there are many words and terms with which you may not be familiar. This exercise introduces most of the common terms, so that you will understand what is going on during open days. Match each of the descriptions below with one of the terms on the right!

DESCRIPTIONS:

1. A student who has not yet completed a degree: _____

2. Students apply for the full degree programme from the beginning: _____

3. Students apply for the full degree programme from the beginning (alternative): _____

4. A session in which students earn marks for doing practical work: _____

5. A week for first years to help them learn about the college and its services: _____

6. A course which serves as an entry point to multiple degree programmes: _____

7. The National Framework of Qualifications _____

8. The equivalent of a 'term' in school: _____

9. A student who is at least 23 years old on the 1st of January in the year of entry: _____

10. A college which awards primarily level 6 awards and higher: _____

11. A college which awards primarily level 7 degrees and higher: _____

12. A self-contained section of a course which covers one topic in detail: _____

13. A level 6 course, worth 2 years of full time studying: _____

14. A level 7 course, typically worth 3 years of full-time studying: _____

15. A level 8 course, typically worth 4 years of full-time studying: _____

16. A full-time 12 to 18 month course usually taken after a bachelor's degree: _____

17. The highest qualification available: _____

18. A student who has successfully completed their first degree: _____

19. A student in the first year of their course: _____

20. A system where marks can be earned throughout the module: _____

21. The UK equivalent of the CAO: _____

22. An exchange programme between colleges in the EU: _____

23. The subject earning more credits in a degree with two subjects: _____

24. The subject earning less credits in a degree with two subjects: _____

25. The introductory first year of a course: _____

26. A session with a more experienced student who assists with coursework: _____

27. A degree with two subjects where equal credits are earned in both subjects: _____

28. A group of modules which are all related to a single subject area: _____

29. The first degree completed by a student: _____

30. A written piece which is submitted for examination, usually in the final year: _____

31. A course which supplements the Leaving Cert and is accepted for entry: _____

32. Further Education and Training: _____

33. A module which doesn't have to be anything to do with your main subject choice: _____

34. A student who has completed a degree and some further studies: _____

Joint Honours

FET

Practical

Graduate

Subject Stream

Fresher

University

Undergraduate

Omnibus Entry

Ordinary Degree

Ab-Initio

Postgraduate

Minor

Module

PhD

Semester

Continuous Assessment

Honours Degree

UCAS

Higher Certificate

Tutorial

NFQ

Conversion Course

Orientation Week

Denominated Entry

Foundation Year

Institute of Technology

Thesis

Mature Entry

Master's Degree

Major

Elective

Bachelor's Degree

Erasmus Programme

Word cloud by wordle.net

Preparation for a college visit

The most important thing about attending open days is to have a plan. There will be a lot of things going on, and it's very easy to forget where things are or which questions to ask. The bigger colleges may have a brochure specifically for the event; smaller colleges may just post information on their website. Either way, get as much information as you can before you set off.

Practical issues

 Get a map of the college. In the larger campuses, or in colleges where the faculties are spread over a number of locations, it is very easy to get lost and waste part of the day. Every year students get lost and miss out – you have been warned! Maps of the college can be obtained from most college websites, or from prospectuses.

 Get a timetable. If this is not available on the college's website, ring or email the college for details. Presentations, lab visits and tours need to be planned for. Often several things are on at the same time, or are repeated hours later, so you will need to know when the events you are interested in are on.

 Get focused. Decide on which courses / departments you are interested in, and spend your time exploring those. Ideally you should have already researched courses and have a shortlist to explore in more depth. If you are still clueless, then give yourself plenty of time to browse around and see if something interests you.

 Bring a friend. Most people will prefer to have someone with them for support – it also helps to share impressions and have someone to take a break with. Parents are also common at open days – they too may need to get a feel for the place and may get answers to their questions (finance, security, accommodation etc.).

Exercise: Open Day Plan

The Open Day Planning Booklet is a handy pocket-sized guide which you can bring to an open day as a reminder of what you want to accomplish during the day. It contains:

» A **day planner** which you can fill with the events that **you** want to visit, where they are, and what time they are on.

» A list of **places and facilities** which you want to visit when you don't have any time pressure; such as the sports centre or library.

» A **list of the courses** which you want to investigate, and the questions you have prepared for the course staff.

» A **list of prompts** in case you find an interesting course which you hadn't planned for and want to find out more about it. Tick the boxes of questions which are particularly important to you.

» Space is reserved for additional **notes and contact details:** don't be afraid to email the college staff to ask for further information!

> Print out an Open Day Planning Booklet for each open day you attend, available to download from the
> **College Open Days App** in the **Career Planning and Research** tab of your **Reach⁺** Career File

DAY PLANNER:

When:	Where:	For:
09:00		
10:00		
11:00		
12:00		
13:00		
14:00		
15:00		

PLACES TO VISIT:

□
□
□
□
□

PROMPTS:

The college in general:
- □ What facilities are available on campus?
- □ Do you have a club or society in [*something you are interested in*]
- □ I will need accommodation; who should I contact for further information?
- □ Can I benefit from any grants?

Comparing colleges:
- □ Which courses do you have in this area?
- □ How do these courses differ from one another?
- □ What facilities do you have, and how do they compare with other colleges?
- □ What links with industry do you have?

About the course:
- □ How many hours of lectures/tutorials/practicals will I have each week?
- □ What is the balance between practical work and lectures?
- □ How big are the class sizes for lectures/tutorials?
- □ Will there be any work placements/internships?
- □ Would I have the opportunity to take part in an exchange programme?
- □ What is the gender balance in this course?
- □ What kind of careers could I get after completing this course?
- □ Do you have any advice in relation to this course?

Applications:
- □ Which Leaving Certificate subjects do I need, and at what level?
- □ I'm weak at maths: would this be a problem?
- □ Is there an interview, supplementary exam, or portfolio?
- □ If I don't make the points, is there an alternative entry route for this course?
- □ Are there fees for this course? When do I need to pay them?
- □ Do I apply directly to the college, or to CAO/UCAS?

COURSES TO INVESTIGATE:

COURSE CODE:	COURSE TITLE:
□	
□	
□	
□	
□	

MY QUESTIONS:

CONTACT DETAILS / NOTES:

Exercise: College Visit Evaluations

College: _____   **Date of Visit:** _____

Departments Visited: _____

Course Name: _____   Course Code: _____

Pros: _____   Cons: _____

_____

_____

What do I need to find out next?

_____

_____

Overall Rating: /10

Course Name: _____   Course Code: _____

Pros: _____   Cons: _____

_____

_____

What do I need to find out next?

_____

_____

Overall Rating: /10

Course Name: _____   Course Code: _____

Pros: _____   Cons: _____

_____

_____

What do I need to find out next?

_____

_____

Overall Rating: /10

Course Name: _____   Course Code: _____

Pros: _____   Cons: _____

_____

_____

What do I need to find out next?

_____

_____

Overall Rating: /10

Personal and Career Values

Everybody has an ideal image in their mind of how they should think and how they should behave. The way you would like to be described in various roles, such as the role of a student, a friend, a son/daughter reveals some of your values and what is important to you. We call the full collection of our values your 'value system'. This system is influenced by your family, friends, school, the media, etc. When we leave school, our set of values will be influenced by new factors such as the way we would like to be described as a worker, a father/mother, a citizen, a professional, etc.

While we may have a wide range of values, when it comes to making choices, some values we hold will prove more important than others. This chapter is about exploring your values and how they matter in the world of work. Some jobs provide scope for expressing what you value, some offer only limited expression, while others may seem to go totally against certain values.

Exercise: Jobs and Values

Are there some things or jobs you would prefer not to do because of what you believe? Are there some jobs you would refuse to do even if they were the only available option? Read the following list of jobs. Tick one box for each job based on how comfortable you would feel doing that job based on your values.

	Supports my values	Neutral to my values	A little against my values	Totally against my values
Parking Clamper				
Forensic Scientist				
Fireman				
Animal Drugs Tester				
Trade Union Official				
Intellectual Disability Nurse				
Bin Collector				
Private Investigator				
Cosmetic Surgeon				
Cigarette Sales Promoter				
Betting Shop Owner				
Politician				
Overseas Charity Worker				
Soldier				
Meat Factory Worker				
Priest				
Tax Inspector				
Human Rights Activist				
Security Guard				
Whaler				
Nuclear Power Plant Engineer				
Your suggestion				
Your suggestion				

Select the three jobs (from the previous page or elsewhere) which would conflict most with your values. Describe below what it is about these jobs that you disagree with.

1. Job Title: _____

   Where my values conflict with this job: _____

   _____

   _____

   _____

   _____

   _____

   _____

   _____

   _____

   _____

   _____

2. Job Title: _____

   Where my values conflict with this job: _____

   _____

   _____

   _____

   _____

   _____

   _____

   _____

   _____

   _____

3. Job Title: _____

   Where my values conflict with this job: _____

   _____

   _____

   _____

   _____

   _____

   _____

   _____

   _____

Exercise: What do you value?

Just as your values are building blocks of your character, they also provide foundations for your career path. As you grew up you learnt many values, and as we have seen from the previous exercise, these can affect your choice of jobs. Knowing what you value helps you to understand your choices, and helps you to make future choices that will be rewarding.

Some people actively plan their career around their values: they will only choose jobs that will allow them to live their values to the full. Others are happy to get by as long as their core values are not ignored, for example, being a victim of injustice, or having their freedom restricted.

In planning your career, choosing jobs which allow you to express your values is the healthiest approach. The more opportunity you get to express what you really believe in, the more rewarding your life will be. What you believe in is likely to change over time, so it is important to reflect on your beliefs and values as they develop. The more your career supports your values, the more job satisfaction you are likely to have.

Read through the list of values on the right, and place the **five** values which are most important to you in the centre of the diagram below. We will call these your **core values**. In each of the outer rings, place any other values you would regard as also being important to you, with the more important ones closer to the centre. If there are any values of yours not on the list, add them in the spaces provided.

Life Values

1.	Belonging:	I want to be accepted by the people around me.
2.	Personal Satisfaction:	I want to feel comfortable with the life I'm living.
3.	Trust:	I want to be able to trust other people and have them trust me.
4.	Self-Esteem:	I want to feel that I am a worthwhile and useful person.
5.	Peace of Mind :	I want to be calm and not be too worried about anything.
6.	Loyalty:	I am responsible in relationships and am willing to make commitments to other people or causes.
7.	Preserving the Earth:	I want to protect nature and the environment for future generations.
8.	Freedom:	I want to be free to make choices without being tied down by other commitments.
9.	Friendship:	I want to get along well with other people and have many friends.
10.	Equality:	I believe in equal opportunities for all people.
11.	Respect for Life:	I do not believe in killing other living creatures.
12.	Children:	I would like to raise or invest time in children.
13.	Eternal Life:	I believe in life after death.
14.	Control:	I want to be able to make influential decisions about my life and the world I live in.
15.	Self-Preservation:	I intend to stay alive for as long as possible.
16.	Enjoyment:	I want to relax and enjoy all of life's pleasures.
17.	Security :	I want to have job, financial, and personal security.
18.	Compassion :	I do my best to help people in need.
19.	Patriotism:	I am loyal to my country and a responsible citizen.
20.	Peace:	I disagree with war, violence, and loss of human life.
21.	Wisdom:	I want to be mature and have a greater understanding of other people.
22.	Family :	I want to raise or be part of a family.
23.	Accomplishment :	I want to achieve impressive things in my lifetime.
24.	Wealth:	I want to have large quantities of money or possessions.
25.	Justice:	I am willing to fight to uphold justice.
26.	Knowledge:	I want to learn more about topics which interest me.
27.	Self Sufficiency:	I want to be able to provide for all my basic needs and support myself financially.
28.		
29.		
30.		

Exercise: Values and Career Choices

+ | add to **Career Portfolio**

Next we will explore how your most important values are likely to be satisfied by careers you may have some interest in exploring further

Choose the five items you value most from the previous exercise and place them in order (most valued at the top) in the **left-most column** of this grid:

	1: Occupation	**2:** Occupation	**3:** Occupation
1: Value	3 2 1 0	3 2 1 0	3 2 1 0
2: Value	3 2 1 0	3 2 1 0	3 2 1 0
3: Value	3 2 1 0	3 2 1 0	3 2 1 0
4: Value	3 2 1 0	3 2 1 0	3 2 1 0
5: Value	3 2 1 0	3 2 1 0	3 2 1 0
Total:			

1. Enter three occupations or general career areas you are considering **across the top** of the grid.

2. Now look at the first of your chosen values and for each career, score how you imagine that career will allow you to express your values by circling the numbers in the grid as follows:

3 = Excellent fit   **2** = Good fit   **1** = Poor fit   **0** = No fit

3. Repeat for each of the remaining values on your list

4. Add up the total scores for each career, and put the total in the box provided.

How do the occupations / career areas you selected match up with your values?

_____

_____

_____

_____

Can you imagine other occupations or career areas that would offer you a better opportunity to grow your values? If so, describe them:

_____

_____

_____

_____

_____

_____

Personality

Everybody has a personality - it's what makes us unique. Our personality is one of the building blocks of who we are – it influences our values, interests, how we learn, what we notice and how well we get on with others. Our personality seems to be partly formed when we are born, and develops and grows according to our experiences.

There are lots of theories about personality and no one theory seems to account for everything. However, one thing which they all agree **on is that you** can't simply match personality to careers. That is to say, there is no one personality type exclusively suited to a specific career. However they all agree that certain jobs may suit some personality types more than others. The phrase that captures this perfectly is "*when he's at work, he's in his element*"

What this phrase means is that the person's work allows them to express their personality fully. It's less to do about what the person does, and more about the opportunity to do it their way, that brings people satisfaction.

In this exercise we will introduce the oldest and most used personality theory of all: **the Four Temperaments.**

Modern day psychologists have made great use of this theory and have used it to help both individuals and some of the world's best known companies. Most employers now believe that workers are far more productive when:

1. They get on well with their co-workers

2. Their personality needs are understood

3. Their strengths are built upon

4. Their differences are accepted

The same applies to students in schools and colleges. In the following exercise we ask you to complete a simple personality inventory - and check to see if an understanding of your personality can guide you in discovering your needs and strengths.

Exercise: Personality Quiz

Read through the questions below and indicate your preference by placing a tick in the grid on the right. If you can't make your mind up on a question, or neither option seems right, skip it.

Note – there are no right or wrong answers, just different preferences!

#	Question				
1	I do most things (a) on the spur of the moment or (b) with a plan in mind	a	b		
2	I prefer looking for (a) what has worked in the past or (b) a new solution		a	b	
3	I take pride in being (a) a creative problem solver or (b) a realistic decision maker		a	b	
4	I prefer to be seen as being (a) sensible or (b) sensitive		a		b
5	Others would describe me as (a) the star of the team or (b) a team player	a			b
6	When I deal with others I tend to act more like (a) a fun friend or (b) a knowledgable friend	a		b	
7	When someone argues with me, it is more important to (a) confront them or (b) make peace	a			b
8	If there is a chance someone's feelings will be hurt by telling the truth I will (a) tell the truth anyway or (b) keep my opinion to myself or "sugar coat" the truth			a	b
9	When I meet my friends I usually ask them (a) what are they doing or (b) how are they feeling		a		b
10	I usually buy clothes (a) for practical reasons or (b) because they make me feel good		a		b
11	My friends would describe me as being more (a) logical or (b) emotional			a	b
12	I'm usually (a) fashionably late or (b) on time	a	b		
13	In relationships I prefer to be more (a) spontaneous or (b) personal	a			b
14	I like to work with (a) my hands or (b) my mind	a		b	
15	When picking movies I usually choose one that is (a) action based or (b) character based	a			b
16	In my daily tasks it's important for me to have (a) change and variety or (b) a set routine	a	b		
17	When faced with an interesting opportunity, I (a) am very enthusiastic at first or (b) take the time to understand more about it first	a		b	
18	In school it is more important for me to (a) have a predictable class or (b) a mentally engaging class		a	b	
19	The way I prefer to cheer up a sad friend is to (a) take them out for a good time or (b) get them to talk about their feelings	a			b
20	In school I learn easier by (a) doing it or (b) reading about it	a		b	

#	Question	Improvisor	Stabiliser	Theorist	Idealist
21	It's more important to (a) follow the rules or (b) make others happy		a		b
22	I learn things better when they are (a) presented with facts (b) told as a heart felt story		a		b
23	At school I prefer to (a) develop my own thoughts or (b) share my thoughts with others			a	b
24	When I am making a decision, I (a) just do it or (b) usually think about it for a while	a		b	
25	I prefer a birthday card that is (a) clever and thought provoking or (b) sentimental			a	b
26	The kind of person I like to spend my time with (a) is fun to be with or (b) makes me think	a		b	
27	I am (a) analysing this test or (b) going with my feelings			a	b
28	When it comes to personal matters in my friendships, I consider it (a) OK to discuss with other friends or (b) too private to discuss	a	b		
29	I prefer someone who would be (a) a practical friend or (b) an intelligent companion		a	b	
30	I prefer to spend time (a) thinking about the things that need to be done now or (b) thinking about future ideas		a	b	
31	I often (a) break the rules or (b) follow the rules	a	b		
32	When I travel I tend to (a) figure out what to do when I get there or (b) have a good plan	a	b		
33	I prefer to be known to others by (a) entertaining them or (b) inspiring them	a			b
34	Most of the time I (a) assume authority is right or (b) question authority		a	b	
35	I am more inclined to (a) think clearly or (b) feel deeply			a	b
36	I prefer to (a) deal with the details needed to complete a task or (b) assist and work with people to get the task done		a		b
	Results:				
		Improvisor	Stabiliser	Theorist	Idealist

Scoring the Profile

To score the profile, simply add up the number of ticks you placed in each of the four vertical columns from both pages of the test. Place the total in the **Results** section at the bottom of the exercise.

> **Note:**
> - This quiz can also be taken online in the **Personality App** from the **Self-Assessment** tab of your **Reach⁺** Career File

Plotting your Personality Profile

Plot your results on the diagram below to create your Personality Profile. On each axis of the profile, mark your score. Then draw lines to connect each of the four scores. The result is a map showing the strengths of each of the four Temperaments that make up your personality.

Theorists

Knowledgable
Analytical and objective
Seeks to understand
Inventive
Abstract
Likes justice and fairness
'Ideas' person
Sets high standards
Problem solver
Independent

Stabilisers

Takes responsibility
Sees practical solutions
Likes to be prepared
Sensible
Punctual and reliable
Makes a loyal friend
Likes rules and directions
Detail conscious
Finishes what is started
Organises well

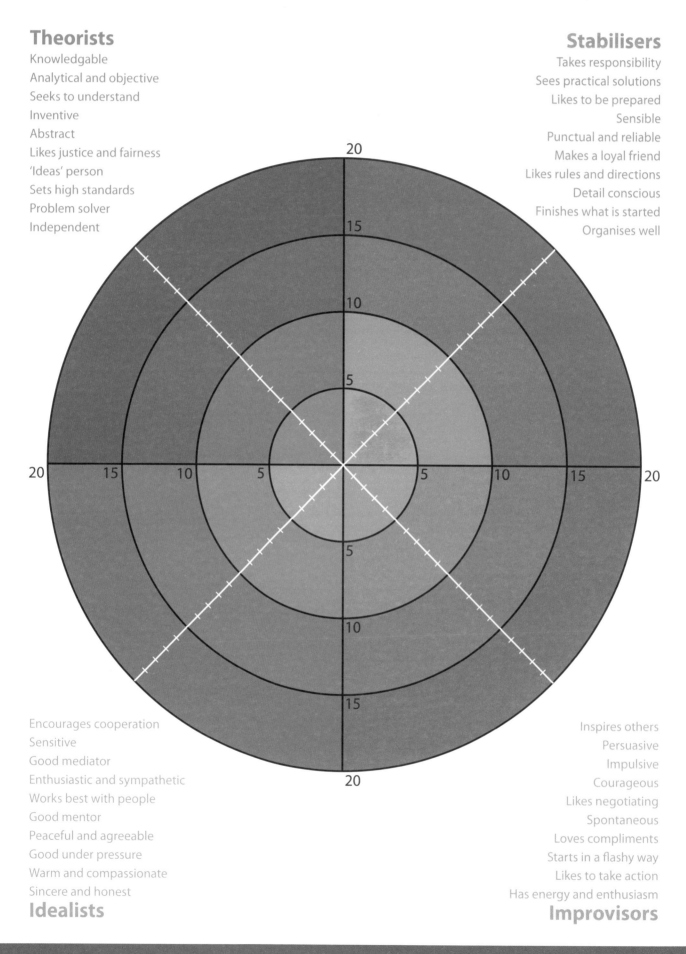

Idealists

Encourages cooperation
Sensitive
Good mediator
Enthusiastic and sympathetic
Works best with people
Good mentor
Peaceful and agreeable
Good under pressure
Warm and compassionate
Sincere and honest

Improvisors

Inspires others
Persuasive
Impulsive
Courageous
Likes negotiating
Spontaneous
Loves compliments
Starts in a flashy way
Likes to take action
Has energy and enthusiasm

Examples:

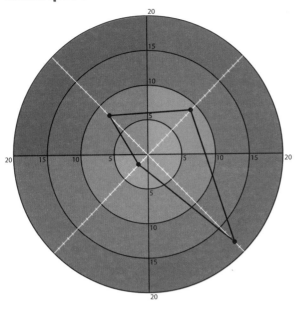

17	9	8	2
Improvisor	Stabiliser	Theorist	Idealist

This example is of someone with strong scores in just one category, the Improvisor. Such a person is likely to be fun loving and always busy doing things. Great at starting things, this person may have a much harder time finishing things off or sticking at things when the going gets tough. With very low Idealist scores this person may be a little fickle and insensitive to the feelings of others.

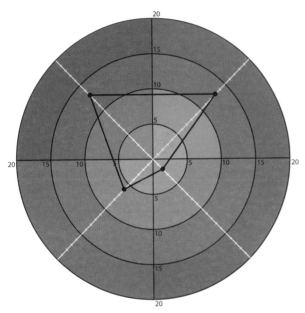

2	13	13	6
Improvisor	Stabiliser	Theorist	Idealist

This is an example of someone who scored strongest in the Theorist and Stabiliser categories. Such a person combines the quick minded qualities of the Theorist with the practical, problem solving attributes of the Stabiliser. Notice the weak Improvisor score – this person may not be naturally good at motivating himself or others, and may be a little 'dry' and serious about life!

Confirm your Temperaments

The exercise provided here should give a good indication of your personality. Next, read about the different Temperaments to confirm which ones describe you best. If your scores from the quiz do not show one Temperament to be strongest, make your decision as to which is strongest having read through the descriptions of each that follows.

Idealist

Idealists are concerned with personal growth and want their life to be meaningful and significant. They like being with people, sharing with them and encouraging them. This is the most philosophical of the four Temperaments and they place a high value on being true and honest with themselves and others. They like to see people grow and develop, and are always ready to help out when a friend needs them.

Idealists are happiest when:

- They have time to reflect on their own personal development and relationships
- They are relating and communicating to others at a deeper than normal level
- They have something to contribute to the world
- They can devote lots of time to whatever meaningful project they are involved in
- They can assist people to get along with each other and work together

Idealists...

- **Dream** of love, affection and authenticity
- **Value** compassion, sympathy and rapport
- **Dislike** hypocrisy, deception and insincerity
- **Respect** nurturing, empathy, and sharing of feelings

Learns best when:

- They are in an open and interactive environment
- Teachers show they care about them personally
- There is harmony and co-operation in the class
- Their feelings are respected
- There is discussion and team-work

Types of Idealists

In his Temperaments theory, David Keirsey* identifies four different types of Idealists as follows:

Teacher: Values organisation, is personal, likes to help people or meet their needs.

Counsellor: Values solitude, is deeply compassionate, desires inner and outer harmony.

Champion: Initiates change, anticipates needs and helps/inspires/encourages others.

Healer: Focuses on personal values, is creative, seeks new ideas and possibilities.

* See www.keirsey.com for more detailed information on Temperaments

Careers

Idealists enjoy jobs that are personally meaningful rather than routine. They value harmony and are not comfortable in competitive positions, although they will stand up for their principles. They prefer to work in organisations that are democratic and that encourage a high degree of participation from all staff. Idealists can be happy in a very wide range of career areas.

Being imaginative, enthusiastic and personable, they can do almost anything that interests them. They are highly creative in dealing with people and are great at inspiring a group spirit and getting people to work together.

They are likely to lose interest in jobs that become routine or lack personal purpose. It is also likely that they are not great with jobs that require a lot of detail and follow-through over a period of time. Their preference is for jobs that allow creativity and variety in day-to-day operations.

They are likely to be attracted to organisations that promote humanistic values or towards jobs that allow them to help others find fulfilment. They may be attracted towards Human Resources and Personnel occupations as well as in Teaching, Consulting, Counselling and the Arts.

Strengths:
- Bring out the best in others
- Resolving conflicts
- Make people feel good about themselves
- Good at giving praise
- Identifying creative solutions to problems
- Warm communication, enthusiastic
- At best can be charismatic, receptive and accepting

Weaknesses:
- Make decisions based exclusively on personal likes and dislikes
- Remaining detached
- Too idealistic and not practical
- Poor at disciplining others
- May sacrifice own opinion just to keep the harmony
- At worst can be moody, unpredictable, over emotional

Interests

Idealists tend to study the humanities. They seek careers facilitating the personal growth of others, whether through education, counselling, or other pursuits that promote the happiness and fulfillment of individuals and society.

Famous Idealists
- James Joyce
- Oprah Winfrey
- Mahatma Gandhi
- Abraham Maslow
- Princess Diana

Stabiliser

Stabilisers value law and order: they like where there are clear rules and guidelines and are driven by a strong motivation to serve our society's needs. They respect authority and the chain of command. They are bound by a sense of duty to do the right thing, which tends to make them reliable, dependable and responsible.

Stabilisers are happiest when:

- They feel responsible and organised
- They belong to a group of like minded friends
- They demonstrate their standards to others
- They make changes carefully and with respect to the past
- They are following rules and cooperating with others

Stabilisers...

- **Dream** of assets, wealth, influence, status and security
- **Value** dependability, accountability and responsibility
- **Dislike** disobedience, non-conformity and cheating
- **Respect** loyalty and obligation

Learns best when:

- The course content is structured and clear
- They know they are on the right track
- They get clear rules and directions
- Their routine is not interrupted

Types of Stabilisers

In his Temperaments theory, David Keirsey* calls this type Guardians, and identifies four different types as follows:

Supervisor: Action orientated, logical, organised, responsible and reliable, likes to finish things.

Inspector: Systematic, thorough, careful, hardworking and good with facts and details.

Provider: Values harmony, can organise people in a warm and compassionate way.

Protector: Values order, is sympathetic, loyal, conscientious and self-sacrificing.

* See www.keirsey.com for more detailed information on Temperaments

Careers

Stabilisers like jobs that involve relatively high levels of responsibility within a stable company with a clear chain of command. They are realistic, matter-of-fact, and more curious about existing products than they are about new ideas and speculation. They like positions that involve following rules and regulations, and prefer when these are clearly defined. They like to be rewarded and valued for their hard work, the responsibilities they take, and the dependability they show.

Stabilisers frequently make good managers. Their thoroughness, practicality, punctuality, and efficiency lead them to occupations where these are appreciated. They have natural talent in managing goods and services, from supervision to maintenance and supply. In these roles they can use all their skills to keep things running smoothly.

Stabilisers have a tendency to be meticulous about schedules and have a sharp eye for proper procedures. They may be cautious about change, even though they know that change can be healthy. Their motto is "look before you leap".

Strengths:

- Practical, organised, thorough and systematic
- Good with regulations and sticking to policies
- Good with proven facts
- Take pride in doing something right the first time and every time
- Resourceful and committed
- At best can be solid, trustworthy and dependable

Weaknesses:

- More focused on the present than the future
- Long range planning may be weak
- May tend to see things only in black and white
- Slow to change and adapt to new ways of working
- At worst, inflexible, dogmatic and unimaginative

Interests

In their education and careers, their primary interest is likely to be in business and commerce, with an eye toward practical applications in management.

Famous Stabilisers

- Queen Elizabeth II
- George Washington
- Warren Buffet
- Ray Kroc
- Mother Teresa

Improvisor

Improvisors seek freedom, independence and adventure. They have a great zest for life and a desire to test their limits. They take pride in developing skills in a variety of fields and don't like to be confined in any way.

Improvisors are excellent negotiators. They tend to focus on the immediate situation and have the ability to assess what needs to be done now. Since they value freedom and spontaneity they seldom choose activities or situations that impose too much structure or too many rules.

Improvisors are happiest when:

- They can act on an idea immediately
- They can use the variety of skills they pick up effectively
- They get involved in new goals and ideas
- They have the opportunity to troubleshoot and solve a problem
- They are under a degree of pressure – "no pain = no gain"
- They have the freedom to choose their own way

Improvisors...

- **Dream** of adventure, spontaneity and being free
- **Value** skills, grace, finesse and charisma
- **Dislike** rigidness, authority and forcefulness
- **Respect** skills and artistic expression

Learns best when:

- Doing!
- There is competition or action involved
- There are games and "hands-on" activities
- There is minimal structure and routines
- They can see how the work can be used in the outside world

Types of Improvisors

In his Temperaments theory, David Keirsey* calls this type Artisans, and identifies four different types as follows:

Promoter: Action oriented, uses a direct, no-nonsense pragmatic approach.

Crafter: Realistic and logical, anticipates immediate practical needs and meets them.

Performer: Friendly, outgoing, fun loving, generous, realistic and lively.

Composer: Gentle, compassionate, quiet, modest, considerate, open and flexible.

Careers

Improvisors are action orientated and are highly resourceful selling a product, idea, or project in a way that other types can't match. They need work that will provide excitement and that doesn't hold them back.

They need to be able to make spontaneous decisions and not have to go through layers of 'red tape'. Their job needs to offer them a good deal of autonomy, variety and action. They prefer to see immediate results and enjoy being able to execute tasks skilfully and successfully.

Though not normally attracted to structured organisations, they may find that their skills in dealing with crises and fast changing situations provide them with a unique role.

Strengths:

- Sees clearly what is happening and is good at seizing opportunities
- Will take risks and improvise when needed
- Respond to changes quickly and are adaptable
- Good observers of human behaviour and good negotiators
- Many are skilful with tools and instruments
- At best they are resourceful, exciting and fun

Weaknesses:

- May not think things through carefully before acting
- Not interested in the more theoretical and abstract aspects of a situation and may miss important connections or patterns that link events
- Tend to lose interest once the crisis phase of a problem is over
- May keep too many options open and miss out on an opportunity

Interests

In education, Improvisors tend to be drawn to the artistic, craft, technical, and athletic subjects and skills that they can use in their career. They tend to seek work involving operations and equipment, which could range from a scalpel to a fighter jet.

Famous Improvisors

- John F. Kennedy
- Madonna
- Mozart
- Clint Eastwood
- Lady Gaga

* See www.keirsey.com for more detailed information on Temperaments

Theorist

Theorists like knowledge and feel best about themselves when solving problems and when their ideas are recognised. They tend to be independent, strong willed, pragmatic and logical. Their idea of a good day is to use their know-how to create solutions.

They are naturally curious, and usually can see many sides to an argument. They are excellent at seeing possibilities, understanding complexities, and designing solutions to real or hypothetical problems.

Theorists are happiest when:

- They feel competent
- They are developing new ideas and expressing them
- They are searching for a greater understanding of something that challenges them
- They are finding ways to improve the way we live in the world

Theorists...

- **Dream** of truth, perfection and accuracy
- **Value** answers, resolutions, intelligence and explanations
- **Dislike** injustice and unfairness
- **Respect** knowledge and competence

Learns best when:

- Exposed to the theory behind the subject
- Working independently
- Exposed to new ideas and concepts
- Provided with a challenge
- Their competence is acknowledged

Types of Theorists

In his Temperaments theory, David Keirsey* calls this type Rationals, and identifies four different types as follows:

Fieldmarshall: Values structure, takes charge, has an analytical/strategic approach to problems.

Mastermind: Strongly individualistic and private, seeks novel ways of looking at things.

Inventor: Values personal freedom/novelty/complexity/change, likes to improvise.

Architect: Values logical clarity, likes to develop concepts and complex ideas.

* See www.keirsey.com for more detailed information on Temperaments

Careers

Theorists need work that allows them to use their ability to see possibilities and analyse them logically to solve problems. They are interested in constantly acquiring knowledge, either for its own sake or for some strategic purpose. They are always on the lookout for new projects, new activities and new procedures.

Suitable jobs are those that provide autonomy, variety, plenty of intellectual stimulation, and the opportunity to contribute their own ideas. They can be impatient with others whom they consider to be less competent than they, and prefer to be surrounded by very capable supervisors, colleagues and friends.

Many Theorists value power and gain influential positions later in their careers. They are equally well at home in college level teaching positions, senior management, science and engineering fields, medicine and law.

Strengths:

- Have great vision and ability to innovate
- Can see possibilities and the bigger picture
- Ability to think forward, plan, and develop systems to reach goals
- Enjoys being challenged, and are demanding of themselves and others
- Can accept criticism without taking it personally
- At best can be confident, witty and imaginative

Weaknesses:

- Overly sceptical and constantly challenge existing rules and assumptions
- May not respect authority
- Often fail to see how they affect others, and may not be interested in the feelings of others
- Can be fiercely competitive and may not bother with a project or activity if they don't think they will excel at it
- At worst, can be arrogant, remote and in a world of their own

Interests

Theorists are drawn to science and technology. They usually seek careers involving systems— whether mechanical (engineering), organic (biology), social (psychology or sociology), or organisational (business or economics).

Famous Theorists

- Marie Curie
- Albert Einstein
- Charles Darwin
- Maria Montessori
- Bill Gates

Exercise: My Personality Reflection

+ | add to **Career Portfolio**

1. What is my strongest temperament?

_____

What is my weakest temperament?

_____

In your own words, describe some of the key characteristics of your temperament.

_____

_____

_____

_____

_____

_____

2. We are all happier and more productive when we are doing a job that fits our temperament. Discuss three characteristics you would now look for in a career that would ensure a good match?

_____

_____

_____

_____

_____

_____

_____

3. Within each of the descriptions of the four temperaments we have included the names of four sub-temperaments. Using your strongest temperament, which of the four sub-temperaments do you think best fits you, and explain why.

_____

_____

_____

_____

_____

_____

_____

Exercise: My Personality Mind Map

Complete a mind map of your personality by drawing more branches and colouring them in. Use words, images and symbols where appropriate. Use one keyword for each new branch you create. Make it colourful!

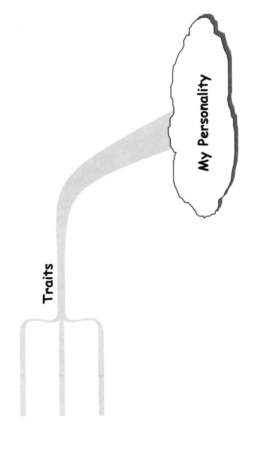

Traits

My Personality

Suggested branches: Strengths, Weaknesses, Interests, Qualities, Values, Likes, Dislikes, Career Characteristics, Needs...

Career Interests

We are born curious – we all want to explore the world around us and enjoy what we see. As we grow up, we tend to be more curious about some things than others, and this reflects something very important in ourselves – our natural interests.

Interests are things you enjoy. Often we are interested in things we are good at, for example someone who plays football well and gets recognition for it is likely to be interested in it.

Sometimes you may be interested in something you haven't yet tried. For example, you may be interested in skydiving but you wouldn't consider yourself to be a skilled skydiver if you have never jumped, or only jumped once. However, if you are willing to learn, you can become skilled at skydiving, you just need to follow up on your interests with the correct training.

Other times you may be interested in something but you may not have the aptitude, talent or personality. You might love to be a singer in a band, but you don't have vocal talent and aren't able to develop the skills needed even with lessons and practice. Instead of singing in a band, you might follow your interest and become involved in some other way – becoming a tour manager, record producer or musician.

Which way for you?
Exploring career interests is one of the most useful ways of finding a career direction. In the exercises that follow, we will explore ways of determining your career interests and how knowing about your interests can be used to help identify career paths.

www.careersportal.ie ⓟ Reach⁺

Exercise: What would I like to do?

A new company is being set up in your area. You have applied to join the company and your application has been successful. It is company policy not to allocate its staff set roles, but as projects and situations arise you will be asked which of the available roles you would like to do most.

Each question presents a situation and offers eight tasks which need to be done. Pick the letters beside the three tasks which you would most like to do, and place those letters in order in the boxes provided, as shown on the right.

Example:

1st	A
2nd	C
3rd	S

You will work the same hours and get the same pay regardless of which choice you make. When making these choices you shouldn't worry about whether you have the necessary abilities, only consider what appeals to you most.

Working Choices

Question 1

Having settled in during the first year, the company are now close to launching a new and innovative product. Market research shows a very positive reaction from the public. You are invited to work on one of the following tasks in preparation for the final launch of the product. Which of the areas below would you most like to work in?

1st	
2nd	
3rd	

A	Making sure staff have all the resources they need to launch the product.
C	Designing the final look of the product packaging.
R	Ensuring all the equipment needed to manufacture the product is fully operational.
S	Introducing new members of staff to their roles, and helping them settle in the company.
E	Motivating management and staff to work on the product.
I	Work out the exact costs of getting the product to market.
L	Give an interview with a science magazine discussing the new product.
N	Working with the catering team to provide the refreshments for the public launch.

Question 2

A major unexpected problem was reported soon after the product was released. Production was stopped and the product was recalled from retail stores. A small but significant number of customers complained of an unusual skin reaction from using the product. Which task would you most like to take on?

1st	
2nd	
3rd	

N	Growing plants to be used in the new product that are known to be free from producing side effects.
E	Meet with the angry directors of the company and persuade them to carry on with the project.
L	Prepare a carefully worded statement for national newspapers on the incident and be prepared to deal with awkward questions from newspaper journalists.
I	Work out the cause of the skin reaction by running extensive tests on the materials that make up the product.
S	Listen carefully to customers complaints and assure customers that the side effects are temporary.
C	Redesign the packaging of the product to distinguish it from the first batch released.
R	Help collect and transport the faulty products back to the company for testing.
A	Carefully document each complaint and research what legal situations might arise.

Question 3

The cause of the skin reaction has been discovered and the product has passed the most rigorous tests. However approval from Company directors is needed to resume production. An emergency international meeting is called at the company's headquarters to persuade the directors that production should go ahead. Which task would you most like to take on?

1st ☐
2nd ☐
3rd ☐

R	Prepare the room for the conference by laying out the tables and chairs or work on serving food and drinks to all those who attend.
S	Welcome the directors as they arrive at the presentation, and introduce them to colleagues with similar backgrounds from around the world.
E	Make a presentation at the conference of the profit forecast based on sales of similar products so that the directors can see how successful it is likely to be.
L	Help write the script for the conference presentation.
C	Design the slides to be used during the conference.
A	Record who is and isn't coming, and make sure that the advice on travel documents needed by directors travelling from abroad is up-to-date and accurate.
I	Show the results of scientific tests and explain clearly why some customers had skin reactions.
N	Work on the landscaping of the grounds and immediate environment in advance of the event.

Question 4

The directors loved the presentation and have decided to move their European headquarters to your site. The factory itself is adequate to cope with production demands, but new offices and administration space is needed. Work should start immediately. Which task would you most like to take on?

1st ☐
2nd ☐
3rd ☐

C	Decide on the layout for the office and pick the colours, furniture, and decoration.
E	Negotiate with the finance department to get more money for the new offices, and then persuade other directors that this is fair and a good use of their money.
S	Arrange a series of social events for staff to compensate for the inconvenience and disruption caused by the construction work.
A	Ensure that all documentation regarding building laws and regulations are dealt with thoroughly so as to avoid any unnecessary delays.
R	Rearrange the existing offices by moving furniture, computers, and filing cabinets to accommodate the new staff until the new offices are ready.
N	Rearrange the landscaping of the grounds to accommodate a new car park and office block.
I	Research new materials that the product could be made from that would make the product smaller, lighter and cheaper to produce.
L	Write a report and do radio interviews on the new developments.

Question 5

Demand for the product has been fantastic so the directors have decided that staff should now be trained in more specialist areas. The following training courses are being offered to you. All courses last the same length of time and all costs of training are covered by the company. Which task would you most like to take on?

1st ☐
2nd ☐
3rd ☐

I	A course in physics and chemistry.
A	A course about commercial law and administration.
C	A course in art and design.
S	A course in social studies or teaching skills.
E	A course in sales and marketing.
R	A course on production machinery, and its maintenance and repair.
L	A course in media studies and communication skills.
N	A course in applied biology and horticulture.

Question 6

A local school has requested a series of presentations for their 3rd year students. The company has agreed. You will need to prepare for the talk and be able to deal with students' questions as best you can. Which kind of talk would you prefer to give?

1st ☐
2nd ☐
3rd ☐

E	Share how wonderful the company is and why they should consider joining when they leave school.
A	Explain how products are shipped abroad efficiently, which shows some of the detailed planning and logistics involved.
I	Discuss how the robotics are programmed to perform high speed tasks on the production line and how to test for faults.
N	Show examples of how destructive a large production plant can be to the environment and how this company strives to eliminate any environmental damage
L	Show the students the importance and impact of a carefully prepared written or oral presentation to the public. Demonstrate the skills involved.
C	Demonstrate the stages which the design team go through when designing an advertisement or brochure, with several examples of works in progress and ads which the students have seen.
S	Show how and why the company goes about attending to the social needs of its workforce.
R	Take students on a tour of the factory and explain to them what each machine does and how it works.

Scoring the Exercise

Enter the number of times that you chose each letter as **first place**:

I	R	E	L	A	N	C	S

Enter the number of times that you chose each letter as **second place**:

I	R	E	L	A	N	C	S

Enter the number of times that you chose each letter as **third place**:

I	R	E	L	A	N	C	S

Add the values in each column and place the **totals** below:

I	R	E	L	A	N	C	S

Now, take the three letters with the highest results and place them in the yellow box below.

Note: If your result does not give you a clear preference order then apply the following scoring procedure. Multiply all your 1st preferences by 3, 2nd preference by 2 and 3rd preference by 1. Recalculate your totals

The company has been observing the choices that you have made and have noted the tasks you show greatest interest in. They now want to collect further information about all their employees' preferences and have the information on file for future use. The personnel department has asked that you fill out the career interest test on the right. When you have completed this, score your results and place the top three letters in the blue box below.

Top three Working Choices:
1. ☐
2. ☐
3. ☐

Top three Interest Results:
1. ☐
2. ☐
3. ☐

Understanding Career Interests

Note any similarities or differences between your 'working choices' while with the company and the results of your interest test. If they are very different, discuss with your Guidance Counsellor.

These exercises are designed to identify areas of interest to you, which are summarised on the following pages. Like most tests and exercises, they don't measure anything very precisely, but they should give a good indication of where your interests lie.

To more fully understand your career interests, read through the descriptions of each of the interest groups that are suggested by the above exercises in the pages that follow. They will describe what they mean and how they relate to occupations and courses that may suit you.

Note: Use the full Interest Profiler App online from your **Reach⁺** Career File to get a more precise measure of your career interests, and use the results to match your interests to occupations and courses.

Exercise: Career Interests

+ add to **Career Portfolio**

Please read both alternatives on each line in the list of activities below. Place a tick in the box marked **A** if you would prefer the activity on the left, or in the box marked **B** if you prefer the activity on the right.

Note: There are no correct or incorrect answers - just differences!

Activity (left)	1	2	3	4	5	6	7	8	Activity (right)
Build something using wood, metal or brick	A		B						Sort out your books or music so they are easy to find
Organise an event down to the last detail				A	B				Work with a Landscape artist in building a newly designed public park
Learn new practical skills	A	B							Manage a business or group of people
Seek new ways to promote a product		A		B					Use a word processor to edit and format documents
Study something in detail	A			B					Use debating skills to present your views
Help a small office become more organised by designing a better filing system				A			B		Visit and chat with old people at a day centre
Drive a van to deliver goods	A				B				Create special effects for a computer game
Use logic to examine whether something is true or false	A	B							Look after machines used in a factory
Help with the wording of slogans used for advertising			A	B					Look after animals in a pet shop
Work the land to improve productivity				A	B				Work with a band/group on a musical performance
Develop better ways to predict something, e.g. the weather, or human behaviour	A				B				Paint a portrait of someone
Repair crashed cars		A					B		Help a survivor of a crash deal with their fears
Use statistical methods to examine the results of a study	A						B		Work with patients in a clinic or hospital
Be an editor of a popular magazine			A				B		Help people with personal or emotional problems
Sell things on eBay		A				B			Propose a design for a new restaurant
Act in a play					A	B			Talk to and comfort someone whose relative has died
Investigate crimes	A	B							Start your own business
Write a song			A	B					Sort files in an office so they are easy to get at
Persuade someone that your view is better		A					B		Listen carefully to hear all sides of an argument
Modify equipment to improve performance		A	B						Give a public speech on a topic you are interested in
Persuade people to join a club or team		A	B						Help in the translation of documents or TV programmes
Examine air quality using scientific test equipment	A			B					Be involved in preparing the yearly budget for a company
Use a computer program to generate customer bills				A		B			Learn to play or practice a musical instrument
Help devise a menu for a new modern multicultural restaurant					A	B			Spend time trying to make new friends
Use mathematical formula to assist in a research project	A			B					Plant and grow seeds in a garden centre
Read good literature				A	B				Design a set for a play
Put electrical parts together in order to make a finished product		A			B				Care for and feed animals in a zoo or farm
Be responsible for selecting people for a team or group activity		A		B					Assist in setting up a fish farm

Results:

I	R	E	L	A	N	C	S

Finally, add up the number of ticks in each of the eight columns and place the letters corresponding to your top three results in the blue box on the previous page.

Interest Groups – What they mean

Group Name:	Code:	In Brief:
Investigative also known as: Analysing, Scientific	I	The Investigative interest is for work that involves solving problems through careful thinking. They tend to be curious about the world, often like to study things, and spend a lot of time in contemplation/ reasoning.
Realist also known as: Practical, Active	R	The Realist interest is for physical or mechanical work. There is usually a hands-on aspect and it is important that there are visible (tangible) results for one's efforts.
Enterprising also known as: Persuasive, Influencing	E	Enterprising people prefer work that allows them to influence what's going on and make decisions. These people like challenging situations and are usually good at motivating others. They are often enthusiastic and ambitious.
Linguistic also known as: Communicating	L	The Linguistic preference is for work involving the creation and exchange of information through books, electronic media, or the spoken word.
Administrative also known as: Conventional, Clerical	A	The Administrative group likes work that involves looking after and organising information and things. People with this preference like clear routines and instructions, and enjoy checking facts and figures. They tend to be well-organised.
Naturalist also known as: Environmental, Organic	N	The Naturalist's preference is for work that involves organic things, such as growing plants, caring for animals, and studying nutrition. Similar to Realists, Naturalists enjoy a hands-on approach and like to see tangible results.
Creative also known as: Artistic, Imaginative	C	The Creative group prefers using their imagination to create something new: a new design, colour scheme, piece of art or music, etc.. People in this group appreciate beauty and are interested in variety - liking unusual sights, sounds, places, people and ideas.
Social also known as: Helping, Advising	S	The Social preference is for work involving direct contact and communication with other people. This may take the form of teaching, helping, serving, or interacting with them in some other way.

Exercise: Occupations and Career Interests

Read through the occupations below and write in the name of the interest group you think is most relevant in the space provided.

The Interest Groups:

Investigative	Realist	Enterprising	Linguistic	Administrative	Naturalist	Creative	Social

Bank Official:
Works behind the counter at a bank branch performing general banking duties.

Fire-fighter:
Responds to emergency calls for all kinds of accidents and disasters including fires.

Chef:
Works in a kitchen preparing food, organising supplies and supervising staff.

Engineer - Software:
Develops, creates, and modifies general computer applications software or specialised utility programs.

Counsellor:
Listens to, supports and tries to help people as they sort out their personal problems.

Set or Costume Designer:
Design costumes and stage sets for television, film and theatrical productions.

Continue by providing **TWO** interest groups for each of the following occupations. For example, an Architect would need the Creative interest to be able to design new buildings, and the Realistic interest to understand how to build and construct safely.

Jeweller:
Designs, sells, and repairs all kinds of jewellery, watches and silverware.

Microbiologist:
Studies and researches micro-organisms like bacteria and algae.

Business Advisor:
Works with client companies to evaluate business plans and optimise long-term costs and production.

Landscape Designer:
Plans, designs and creates new landscapes to meet customers expectations while complying with environmental constraints.

Aeronautical Engineer:
Employed in the designing, testing and making of aircraft engines and other such aeronautical productions.

Surgeon:
A qualified medical doctor who specialises in performing surgery for patients who need an operation.

Outdoor Activities Instructor:
Works with people on outdoor activity sessions and trips, or teachs them skills in a wide range of outdoor activities.

Exercise: Class Interests Profile

What is the distribution of first preferences in your class?

Find out how many students in your class have first preferences in each of the interest groups. Enter the number for each in the table (right).

Investigative: _____
Realist: _____
Enterprising: _____
Linguistic: _____
Administrative: _____
Naturalist: _____
Creative: _____
Social: _____

Fill in the following graph to visually display the most popular interest groups in your class.

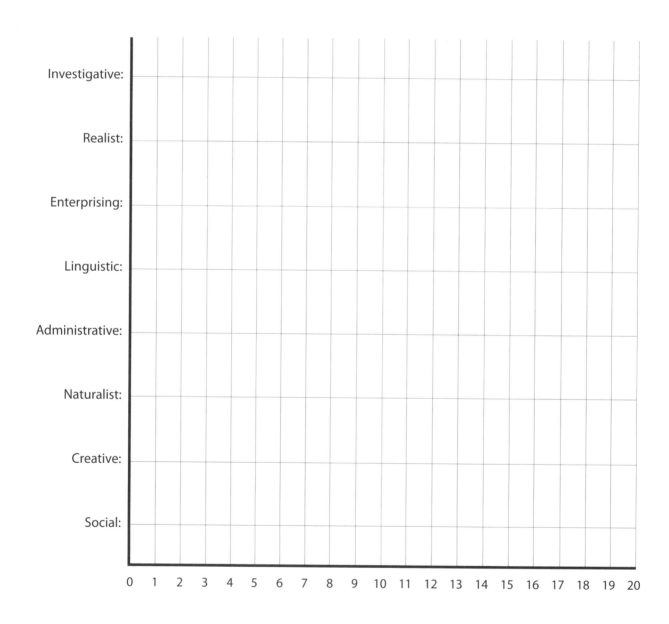

Career Interests - What they mean

The following pages contain descriptions of 8 career interest types, along with sample occupations, CAO and PLC courses that are related to them. Using the results of the previous exercises to guide you, read through the descriptions to establish your career interests. Once you have decided on your interests, complete the questions at the end of these descriptions.

 Reach+

Investigative

General

Investigative types like working with ideas and prefer occupations that require an extensive amount of thinking. They like searching for facts and figuring out problems mentally. They have a scientific approach to everything, believing that with enough knowledge all problems would be solved.

Interests

The Investigative person will usually find a particular area of science to be of interest. They are inclined toward intellectual and analytical activities and enjoy observation and theory. They may prefer thought to action, and enjoy the challenge of solving problems with sophisticated technology. These types prefer mentally stimulating environments and often pay close attention to developments in their chosen field.

Activities

Investigative activities may include collecting information for analysis (e.g. Financial Analyst), developing or using classification systems to assist with large amounts of data (e.g. Botanist), using mathematical formulae to predict outcomes (e.g. Statistician), designing and carrying out research work (e.g. Forensic Scientist), determining causes and effects (e.g. Doctor, Dietician), and using scientific procedure to investigate complex problems (e.g. Biochemist, Astronomer).

Sample Careers:

Radiographer
Engineer - Energy
Naturopath
Doctor
Economist
Surgeon
Engineer - Polymer
Dentist
Laboratory Technician
Engineer – Marine
Orthodontist
Paediatrician
Scientist
Computer System Administrator
Forensic Scientist
Engineer - Chemical
Neurologist
Geologist
Statistician
Chiropractor

Sample PLC Courses:

Computer Games Development
Computer Science
Applied Science
Business IT
Information Processing - Computer Applications
Computer Games & Interactive Entertainment
Software Engineering
Laboratory Science
Applied Science - Laboratory Techniques
App Development

Sample CAO Courses:

Theoretical Physics and Mathematics
Computing
Medicine
Mathematics
Instrument Engineering
Business Information Systems
Computer Science
Science
Psychology
Arts - Mathematical Physics

Realist

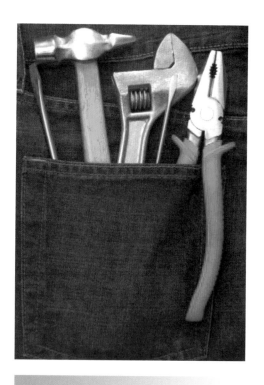

General

The Realist interest is for work that involves 'doing' something to inanimate 'things'. There is usually a hands-on aspect to this work, and it is important that there are visible (tangible) results for one's efforts.

Interests

Realists are usually interested in 'things' - such as buildings, mechanics, equipment, tools, electronics etc. Their primary focus is dealing with these - as in building, fixing, operating or designing them. Involvement in these areas leads to high manual skills, or a fine aptitude for practical design - as found in the various forms of engineering.

Realists like to find practical solutions to problems using tools, technology and skilled work. Realists usually prefer to be active in their work environment, often do most of their work alone, and enjoy taking decisive action with a minimum amount of discussion and paperwork.

Activities

Realist activities include basic physical work (handling goods, deliveries), controlling and operating equipment (e.g. cranes, aircraft), using tools and instruments (drills, microscopes), building and repairing equipment (e.g. construction work, electrics, electronics, mechanics), skilled labour (e.g. precision cutting/alignment) and other work requiring fine eye-hand coordination (e.g. sports, pilot).

Sample Careers:

Insurance Surveyor
Lifeguard
Deckhand
Carpenter / Joiner
Paramedic
Exercise and Health Instructor
Plumber
Engineer – Electrical
Engineer - Civil
Agricultural Mechanic
Motor Mechanic
Air Corps Cadet
Hotel Porter
Modelmaker
Carpet/Vinyl Fitter
Dental Technician
Metal Fabricator / Welder
Electronic Equipment Assembler
Factory Assembler / Lineworker
Surveyor, Building / Mining

Sample PLC Courses:

Cabinet Making & Construction
Computers - PC Maintenance
Electronic Technology
Engineering Technology
Exercise & Health Fitness
Motor Technology
Networks & Software Systems
Outdoor Recreation
Security Studies
Construction Technology

Sample CAO Courses:

Engineering - Mechanical
Engineering - Computer
Furniture Design and Manufacture
Computer Networks and Systems Management
Aviation Management / Aviation Management with Pilot Studies
Network Technologies
Architectural Technology
Engineering - Electronic
Mobile Communications and Electronics
Construction Management

Enterprising

General

Enterprising types like situations and work that involves starting up and carrying out projects. These types like challenging situations and are usually good at leading or motivating others. They are often enthusiastic and ambitious.

Interests

Enterprising people like situations that involve using resources for personal or corporate economic gain. Such people may have an opportunistic frame of mind, and are drawn to commerce, trade and making deals. Some pursue sales and marketing occupations. Many will eventually end up owning their own business, or in management roles in larger organisations. They tend to be very goal-oriented and work best when focused on a target. Some have an entrepreneurial inclination.

Activities

Enterprising activities may include general sales work (e.g. dealing with customers, recommending products), motivating others on projects (e.g. supervising), developing goals for an organisation (e.g. Manager), exploring new ways to deal with old problems (e.g Management Consultants), predicting future trends and patterns (e.g. Business Analyst), prioritising over multiple tasks, taking risks, and managing one's own business (e.g. Business Owner).

Sample Careers:

Detective Inspector
Hairdresser
Wholesaler
Marketing Adviser
Fundraiser
Stores Manager
Fund Manager
IT Consultant
Business Advisor
Hotel - General Manager
School Principal
Events and Promotions Manager
Solicitor
Purchasing Manager
International Sales Representative
Estate Agent
Sales Assistant
Shop Manager
Accounts Team Leader
Production Manager - Film

Sample PLC Courses:

Marketing
Web Marketing & Sales
Auctioneering
Enterprise Education - Business Studies
Management - Sport and Recreation
Start Your Own Business
International Trade
Event Management with TV Studies
Entrepreneurial Studies
Retail Practice
Marketing & Sales

Sample CAO Courses:

International Development and Food Policy
Marketing Innovation and Technology
Business Information Systems
Business Studies
Accountancy and Finance
Business - Human Resource Management
Travel & Tourism Management
Business, Economic and Social Studies
Bar Management and Entrepreneurship
Computing Systems Management

66 Linguistic

General

Linguistic types enjoy work involving the creation and exchange of information through writing, electronic media or the spoken word. These people prefer unstructured environments where there is time to use their imagination to compose their words and thoughts, and time to express and communicate what they feel.

Interests

The Linguistic's interests are usually focused on ideas and information exchange. They tend to like reading a lot, and enjoy discussion about what has been said. Some will want to write about their own ideas and may follow a path towards journalism, story writing or editing. Others will develop skills in other languages, perhaps finding work as a translator or interpreter. Most Linguistic types will enjoy the opportunity to teach or instruct people in a topic they are interested in.

Activities

Linguistic activities include writing and reworking text to make it more presentable to certain audiences (e.g. Editor, Technical Writer), evaluating and assessing documents (e.g. Critic, Script Writer), exploring alternative media to express and present ideas (e.g. Media Executive, Multimedia Writer), creative writing (e.g. Author), translation of written or spoken material, creative expression of a script (e.g in drama, acting), and skilled wording of material for persuasive, technical or entertainment purposes (e.g. Lawyer, Radio & TV Presenter).

Sample Careers:

Barrister
Broadcast Journalist
Corporate Affairs Manager
Court Reporter
Editor - Publishing
Interpreter
Journalist / Reporter
Linguist
Engineer - Localisation
Marketing / Communications Manager
Multimedia Writer
Proof Reader
Public Relations Account Executive
Software Localisation Technician
Technical Writer
Television/Radio Presenter
Translator
Writer
Advertising Copywriter
Copy Editor

Sample PLC Courses:

Journalism
Media Production
Creative Media Production - Journalism
Media Production - Creative Writing & Cultural Studies
Print Journalism
Language & European Studies
English & European Studies
Digital Media
Media Production - TV & Film
Journalism with Photography

Sample CAO Courses:

Applied Languages
Arts – with Language
BA International with French
Communications and Public Relations
Journalism
Irish and New Media
Language, Literature and Film
Media Studies
Classics
Humanities

Administrative

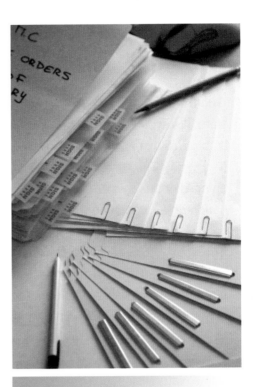

General

Adminstrative types like work that involves looking after and organising items and information. These people like clear routines and instructions, and enjoy checking facts and figures. They are comfortable following well-defined rules and enjoy work that involves organisation and routine.

Interests

Administrative people are interested in work that offers security and a sense of being part of a larger process. They may be at their most productive under supervisors who give clear guidelines and while performing routine tasks in a methodical and reliable way.

They tend to enjoy clerical and most forms of office work, where they perform essential administrative duties. They often form the backbone of large and small organisations alike. They may enjoy being in charge of office filing systems, and using computers and other office equipment to keep things running smoothly. They usually like routine work hours and prefer comfortable indoor workplaces.

Activities

Administrative activities may include general office organisational work (filing, photocopying, typing), processing information using forms (e.g. evaluating information for suitability, availability), implementing procedures (e.g. mailshots), organising activities and events (e.g. secretarial work), collecting and sorting data (e.g. accounts, forms), using mathematical procedures (e.g. cash flow analysis, market forecasting), logging activities and performance (e.g. Law Clerk, Medical Secretary).

Sample Careers:

Airport Check-in Agent
Pensions Administrator
Accountant / Tax Expert
Checkout Operator
Secretary
Library/Information Assistant
Insurance Claims Advisor / Manager
Accounts Administrator
Auditor
Business Consultant
Bank / Financial Manager
Bookkeeper / Numerical Clerk
Business Analyst
Curator/Keeper (Museum/Art Gallery)
Bank Official
Filing / Records Clerk
Data Input Operator
Lawyer
Civil Service - Clerical Officer Law Clerk
Civil Service - Higher Executive Officer
Auditor

Sample PLC Courses:

Business & Marketing
Business - Enterprise Studies
Occupational Safety & Health
Laboratory Techniques
Business & Secretarial Studies
Business Studies
Office Administration Skills
Accounting Technician
Administration
eBusiness - Business Information Systems

Sample CAO Courses:

Business Studies
Business and Law
Quantity Surveying
Commerce (European) With Spanish
Logistics & Supply Chain Management
Law (Clinical)
Financial Services
Property Economics (Valuation Surveying)
Legal Studies
Arts - Economics

Naturalist

General

Naturalist types like work that involves 'doing' something to 'organic things', i.e. plants, animals and their produce (e.g. food). They like work that may involve nurturing plants, animals or the environment. Like Realists, Naturalists enjoy a hands-on approach and like to see tangible results.

Interests

Not surprisingly, some aspect of the natural sciences will run through the Naturalist's interests - from ecological awareness to nutrition and health. People with an interest in horticulture, land usage and farming (including fish) are Naturalists.

Some Naturalists focus on animals rather than plants, and may enjoy working with, training, caring for, or simply herding them. Other Naturalists will prefer working with the end result of nature's produce - the food produced from plants and animals. Naturalists like solving problems with solutions that show some sensitivity to the environmental impact of what they do. They like to see practical results and prefer action to talking and discussing.

Activities

Naturalist activities may include basic physical work (cleaning animals, planting, food preparation), managing animal and/or plant welfare (e.g. breeding, propagation, spraying), using an understanding of natural life-cycles to optimise productivity (as with crops, forestry and herding), using knowledge of foodstuffs to produce commercial food produce (e.g. Butchers, Confectioners), the preparation, cooking and serving of food (e.g. Chefs and their assistants).

Sample Careers:

Zoo Keeper
Environmental Technician
Gardener
Farm Manager
Pastry Chef
Agricultural Adviser
Cartographer
Fisherman/woman
Groundsman/woman
Pet Shop Worker
Forester - Professional
Fishmonger
Brewer
Veterinary Surgeon
Veterinary Nurse
Farmer - Dry Stock
Park Warden / Officer
Baker/Confectioner
Jockey
Butcher

Sample PLC Courses:

Garden Design
Agriculture
Animal Science
Applied Ecology
Greenkeeping & Sports Turf Management
Horticulture
Organic Gardening
Food Science
Culinary Skills
Hotel & Catering

Sample CAO Courses:

Horticulture
Spa Management
Culinary Arts
Environmental Science and Health
Biochemistry and Molecular Biology
Dairy Business
Agricultural Science
Health and Nutrition for Culinary Arts
Animal Science
Forestry

Creative

General

Creative types like work that involves using personal imagination to create something new - a new design, colour scheme, piece of art or music etc. These types enjoy beauty, and are interested in variety - liking unusual sights, sounds, places, people and ideas.

Interests

Creative people are drawn to careers and activities that enable them to take responsibility for the design, layout or sensory impact of something (visual, auditory etc). They may be atrracted to the traditional artistic pursuits such as painting, sculpture, singing, or music. Or they may show more interest in design activities, such as architecture, animation, or craft areas, such as pottery and ceramics.

Creative people use their personal understanding of people and the world they live in to guide their work. Creative people like to work in unstructured workplaces, enjoy taking risks and prefer a minimum of routine.

Activities

Creative activities may include exploring colour, shape, composition, and rhythm (e.g. fine art, music), exploring the space we live in and the materials we use (e.g. Architect), using one's sensitivity to people's needs in order to design and decorate places or people (e.g. Interior Designer, Beautician, Fashion Designer), or refining physical skills (e.g. Singer, Sculptor, Potter, Mime Artist).

Sample Careers:

Architect
Animator
Graphic Artist
Creative Director
Make-Up Artist
Film/Video Tape Editor
Model
Dressmaker
Beautician
Set or Costume Designer
CAD Technician
Camera Operator
Web Designer
Photographer
Artist
Musician
Technical Illustrator
Actor/Actress
Potter
Singer

Sample PLC Courses:

Graphic Design
Architectural Technology
Art - Craft - Design
Computer Aided Design
Creative Craft - Jewellery & Art Metalcraft
Make Up Artistry
Furniture Making & Restoration
Interior Design
Multimedia Production - Graphic Design
Digital Marketing

Sample CAO Courses:

Music Technology
Media Arts
Entertainment Systems
Performing Arts (Acting)
Music Performance
Design for Stage and Screen (Costume Design)
Multimedia (Computing and Design)
Film and Media
Visual Communications and Design
Interior Architectural Technology

Social

General

Social types enjoy spending lots of time with people, and often make a profession out of providing some form of care or assistance to them. They like a work environment where they meet and discuss issues that concern individuals, often in a supportive and nurturing role.

Interests

The Social person's interests focus on interacting with the people in their environment. In all cases, the Social person enjoys the personal contact of other people in preference to the impersonal dealings with things, data and ideas found in other groups.

Many will seek out positions where there is direct contact with the public in some advisory role, whether a receptionist or a counsellor. Social people are motivated by an interest in different types of people, and like diversity in their work environments. Many are drawn towards careers in the caring professions and social welfare area, whilst others prefer teaching and other 'informing' roles.

Activities

The Social person's activities may include being receptive to others' needs (e.g Hospitality Assistant, Nurse), giving information and general guidance (e.g. Driving Instructor), teaching (e.g. School Teacher), listening and collecting information (e.g. Garda, Care Worker), providing professional guidance (e.g. Counsellor, Legal Advisor), and negotiating, mediating and resolving conflicts (e.g. Probation Officer).

Sample Careers:

Nurse - General
Occupational Therapist
Art Therapist
Acupuncturist
Speech & Language Therapist
Social Worker - Health Care
Guidance Counsellor
Psychiatric Nurse
Nursery / Playgroup Teacher
Nurse - Intellectual Disability
Probation Officer
Care Assistant
Garda
Counsellor
Physiotherapist
Childcare work
Teacher - Physical Education
Dental Nurse/Surgery Assistant
Primary School Teacher
Crèche Assistant

Sample PLC Courses:

Community Care - Pharmacy Assistant
Childcare
Special Needs Assistant
Sport & Recreation - Sports Coaching
Hairdressing
Nursing Studies
Sports Therapy
Tourism - Airline Studies - Cabin Crew
Community & Health Services
Healthcare Support

Sample CAO Courses:

Health and Social Studies
Psychology
Early Childhood Care and Education
Psychiatric Nursing
Applied Social Studies - Social Care
Community and Social Development
Education, Irish and Religious Studies
General Nursing
Midwifery
Philosophy

Exercise: Career Interests Reflection

Which career interest group best describes you and why?

_____

_____

_____

_____

_____

_____

_____

Which other career interest groups also describes you and why?

_____

_____

_____

_____

_____

_____

_____

_____

_____

_____

What career or course possibilities would match up well with your

career interests? _____

_____

_____

_____

_____

_____

_____

_____

_____

_____

Aptitudes & Intelligences

What is an Aptitude?

An aptitude is a natural talent, capacity, or ability to do or learn something. Having an aptitude for something means you are good at it.

What Are Aptitude Tests?

An aptitude test measures a person's aptitude for a particular task. These tests have been around for years, and are useful because they have been performed on large groups of people spanning many age groups and backgrounds. They are used to compare individuals from a similar age group and gender, and the results can give a good idea of how a person performs on a range of tasks compared to their peers.

Aptitude testing is popular amongst employers and career professionals for a number of reasons. They can be used by companies to screen for employees who have an aptitude for things they might need to do on the job. For example, a company hiring an accountant might ask applicants to take an aptitude test to test mathematical ability.

When used in guidance counselling, aptitude tests offer a second opinion alongside your exam results to help suggest areas you might be interested in. This could be helpful for picking college courses, or when choosing subjects for the Leaving Certificate.

Aptitude Tests in Schools

Not all schools use aptitude tests, but if yours does it is most likely to be the CAT4 or the Cambridge Profile Aptitude Tests. These tests measure different types of ability, or aptitude, which may be related to success in different areas of employment. They provide a profile which shows the relative strengths and weaknesses in a person's key aptitudes.

Tests are taken over several hours in controlled conditions and supervised by a guidance counsellor. This chapter may help you to get the most out of your results, which will be given to you by your school some time after you take the test. Research shows that aptitude tests have the following qualities:

Qualities of Aptitude Tests:
- They are excellent predictors of future academic achievement.
- They provide ways of comparing a student's performance with that of other students in the same situation, e.g. the same age, sex, culture.
- They provide a profile of strengths and weaknesses.
- They have uncovered hidden talents in some students, thus improving their educational opportunities.

Note:
- More information and sample questions are available from the **Aptitudes App** in the **Self-Assessment** tab of your **Reach⁺** Career File

Exercise: My Aptitudes

This exercise requires you to have the results of your aptitude test, and to know the rank order (from highest scoring to lowest) of the results. Note that your actual scores are not important for this exercise – just the order from highest to lowest.

Aptitude tests are made up of a number of sub-tests. Enter in the table below the name of your highest scoring sub-test in the first row, followed by the second highest in the second and so on.

	Aptitude:
1st	
2nd	
3rd	
4th	
5th	
6th	
7th	
8th	

Using the Results

The results of your test enable you to see how you did in a range of different aptitudes. Some aptitudes are likely to be better developed than others, and this suggests that you are more naturally skilful and strong in those areas. Others are less well developed, and choosing subjects, courses and jobs that require high ability in these areas may be more challenging for you.

The descriptions of the typical sub-tests that follow will give you a better idea of what each of the individual aptitudes mean and of how an understanding of each can help you in choosing a career you are suited to. Usually students follow subjects and careers that build on their talents and best abilities, but this is not necessarily the case. The tests aren't perfect and don't measure everything, so it is critical to combine the information here with several other measures of your ability, skills and interests.

Many students are pleasantly surprised with their aptitute test results – as they can show strengths in areas that they have not considered before. At the end of the descriptions you can write a **short summary of what your results mean for you**.

Read through the descriptions of sub-tests for the aptitude test you took, starting with the one you scored highest in. Reflect on this information with regard to your current thoughts on your career direction and subject choices, and complete the summary at the end.

Verbal Reasoning

Verbal reasoning refers to the ability to reason with words, and to understand and use concepts expressed in words.

An average score means you should feel fairly comfortable working with ideas expressed in verbal form. You will probably also be reasonably good at expressing yourself in words. Verbal Reasoning ability is important for any work involving the communication of ideas or the interpretation of written material. It can also be important for many kinds of work, in which analytical thinking is required.

Areas of work in which these abilities are required are professional jobs (e.g. Lawyer, Doctor, Teacher), technical jobs (e.g. Engineer, Computer Programmer), business (e.g. management, sales, marketing and advertising), scientific work and also many fields of work in which communication is of primary importance (e.g. training, work involving the production of written material and administrative positions).

It is also important to have fairly good verbal skills if you wish to undertake further training or study, especially in one of the more academic fields.

Possible Subjects:
- English
- History
- Languages
- LCVP Link Modules
- Music, Art
- Religious Education
- Geography
- Home Economics
- Politics & Society

Numerical Reasoning / Quantitative Reasoning

Numerical reasoning measures the ability to reason with numbers and to deal intelligently with quantitative measures.

It is important for work in the technical professions such as science, engineering and architecture. It is also important for many jobs in business and finance (e.g. sales forecasting, banking, etc) and is very much needed for work in accounting.

In the technical area, Numerical Reasoning is relevant to any sort of work in which calculations or precise measurements need to be made (e.g. surveying, navigation, joinery or laboratory work). It is also important for many clerical or administrative jobs (e.g. local government, accounts administration, etc.).

Possible Subjects:
- Maths
- Physics
- Chemistry
- Applied Maths
- Accounting
- Economics

Abstract Reasoning / Non Verbal Reasoning

This aptitude test measures a person's ability to reason with abstract ideas, and is a measure of non-verbal, non-numerical reasoning power. It is concerned with being able to perceive patterns among complex elements and to be able to see how those elements relate to each other, for example, patterns, diagrams or designs rather than words and numbers.

The ability to think in abstract terms is needed for work which involves seeing relationships between things; either in a logical sense or in a practical sense. It is therefore useful for fields such as computer programming and software design, mathematics, science and engineering. It can also be useful in areas such as technical maintenance, which involves understanding how parts of a machine or system relate to one another.

Abstract reasoning is also important for working in the field of design, since design is often concerned with the expression of abstract ideas or themes. Finally, abstract reasoning can also be very important in management, especially at the higher levels where one needs to see how the different parts of a complex organisation fit together.

Possible Subjects:

- Physics
- Chemistry
- Biology
- Music
- History
- Art
- Applied Maths
- Computer Science
- Technology
- Design and Communication Graphics

Perceptual Speed and Accuracy / Working Quickly and Accurately

This aptitude measures the ability to work accurately with detail and at speed. Such an ability is important in many kinds of detailed work (letter writing, form filling, filing records and entering information into a computer, i.e. most office work) and is also quite important for scientific or technical work where precision is required (e.g. computer programming or laboratory work).

Furthermore, this is an ability required in all work where attention to detail and quality are important (e.g. accountancy, surgery, forensics and some types of legal work). As this aptitude measures speed and accuracy, low scores may occur as a result of a greater emphasis on correctness rather than a genuine lack of ability to work rapidly.

Possible Subjects:

- All subjects
- Especially important for exam performance!

Mechanical Reasoning

The mechanical reasoning test measures the ability to understand the basic principles of machinery, of tools, and of physical relationships between things.

This ability is important for any sort of work involving the design, operation, or repair of equipment and is also very important in the field of engineering and in some areas of product design.

Examples of jobs in which mechanical ability is important include Motor Mechanic, Gas Fitter and Repairer, Industrial Fitter, Production Engineer, Civil Engineer, Aeronautical Engineer, Surveyor, Eectrician, Carpenter, Machine Operator, Product Designer and Builder.

Possible Subjects:

- Physics
- Applied Maths
- Construction Studies
- Engineering
- Technology
- Design and Communication Graphics
- Agricultural Science

Space Relations / Spacial Ability

The space relations test assesses a person's ability to visualise objects in three dimensions.

This ability is needed for any form of work in which it is important to be able to visualise objects and to understand how they relate to each other. Examples of job areas where good spatial abilities are required include architecture, design, technical drawing, dentistry, the fine arts, and also any type of technical or craft work.

Possible Subjects:

- Art
- Home Economics
- Design and Communication Graphics
- Construction Studies
- Engineering
- Technology

Language Usage: Grammar

This is a measure of how well you can distinguish between correct and incorrect grammar, punctuation, and capitalisation. It is an excellent predictor of grades in both school and college courses, i.e. if you score highly in this aptitude, you are likely do well at school and college in general.

While such careers as writing and teaching require especially well developed language skills, nearly all kinds of work requiring college-level education demand a considerable competence in this area. Examples of areas in which good language skills are required include management, teaching, professional work (e.g. Medicine, Law, Accountancy), work in the media (Radio and Television, Journalism) and all forms of clerical / administrative work.

Possible Subjects:

- All Science, Business, and Languages
- History
- Geography
- Home Economics
- Religious Education
- Politics & Society

Language Usage: Spelling

The spelling test measures your capability to recognise correctly or incorrectly spelled common English words.

This is an important skill in school, college and many jobs where there is an emphasis on writing. It is useful to compare this score with your score in Verbal Reasoning. If your Spelling and Grammar scores are much lower than Verbal Reasoning, then you may benefit from extra study or tutoring to help improve your English language skills. Otherwise your exam marks are unlikely to reflect your actual ability.

Possible Subjects:

- All Science, Business, and Languages
- History
- Geography
- Home Economics
- Religious Education
- Politics & Society

Exercise: My Aptitudes Reflection

1 Do you think your aptitude test accurately reflects your top aptitudes? Discuss your answer.

_____

_____

_____

_____

_____

_____

_____

2 Were you surprised by any of the results? If so which ones and why were you surprised?

_____

_____

_____

_____

_____

_____

_____

3 Do the results support (agree with) your choice of subjects or career ideas? Discuss.

_____

_____

_____

_____

_____

_____

_____

_____

_____

_____

_____

_____

Intelligences

What is Intelligence?

You may have heard of a person's IQ – a score that is supposed to tell you how intelligent a person is. Really brainy people would often boast that they had a high IQ – usually just annoying everyone else in the room – which, oddly enough, is not very intelligent!

Intelligence Tests (IQ Test) score people on a variety of activities and creates a profile of a person's abilities, similar to an aptitude test. It is a great tool used mostly by psychologists to identify specific learning differences and to help people find ways to overcome them. It measures a limited number of abilities, and so misses many important characteristics that make up a person.

The modern theory of 'multiple' intelligences' offers a broader perspective on intelligence, and helps us to understand how we learn best and why we are interested in some things more than others. Nowadays, people find it more helpful to ask "how are you intelligent?" than "how intelligent are you?"

The good news is that we all have multiple intelligences. Even better – we all have a different mix of stronger and weaker ones. This means we all learn differently, have different interests and skills, and life is much more interesting!

One person may find understanding mathematics and logical problems easy, another person is more natural composing music and rhythms, and another seems to understand living creatures and nature without effort. Equally brainy – but different!

The Eight Intelligences:

Name:	Brief Description:
Linguistic-Verbal	Good with Words – Word Smart
Logical-Mathematical	Good with Mathematics and Logic – Number Smart
Musical	Good with Rhythm – Music Smart
Bodily-Kinesthetic	Good with Activities – Body Smart
Spatial	Good with Art and Design – Picture Smart
Interpersonal	Good with Communication – People Smart
Intrapersonal	Good at Self-Reflection – Self Smart
Naturalist	Good with Understanding Natural World – Nature Smart

It would be really useful to know which of our intelligences is the strongest, but this is difficult to measure, especially using written tests. This is because written tests require people to read, and favour people who love words. How can we test your physical dexterity (e.g. ability to catch a ball) or musical ability (tap a complex rhythm) or interpersonal skills (comforting someone who is upset) using a written test?

Answer: *We can't!*

However, we can ask you some questions about yourself and get some clues: this is a start at least. So try our MI questionnaire and see if you agree with the results. It tries to find out which are your strongest intelligences, and gives you a report on what it finds. As you read through the descriptions you may agree or disagree with what is said. We recommend you form your own conclusions and write these into your workbook.

Exercise: Multiple Intelligences

#1. Read through the items and place a circle around the response you agree most with.

#2. In the right hand columns, enter the value you circled into the white space for each answer.

#3. Add up the values in each column to reveal the score for each of the eight categories.

Response scale (left to right): Strongly Disagree (1), Disagree (2), Neutral (3), Agree (4), Strongly Agree (5)

Right-hand scoring columns: a b c d e f g h

#	Statement	SD	D	N	A	SA
1.	I often find myself humming silently to myself	1	2	3	4	5
2.	I love to be physically active - e.g. in sports, dance, adventuring	1	2	3	4	5
3.	I prefer team sports	1	2	3	4	5
4.	I find graphs and charts easer to understand than words and plain numbers	1	2	3	4	5
5.	Music is very important to me and I find that it can leave me with strong emotions	1	2	3	4	5
6.	I like to watch natural phenomena, such as the moon and the tides	1	2	3	4	5
7.	I nearly always notice when others make a grammatical mistake when they talk or write	1	2	3	4	5
8.	I often dream of designing buildings or things and can visualise these things easily	1	2	3	4	5
9.	I often create melodies or rhythms in my mind and hum or tap them out	1	2	3	4	5
10.	I find it easy to think up stories and enjoy writing things down	1	2	3	4	5
11.	I'm good at picking out different instruments when I listen to music	1	2	3	4	5
12.	I enjoy logic problems and puzzles and brainteasers	1	2	3	4	5
13.	I always know my friends moods and easily adjust to them	1	2	3	4	5
14.	Games that require lots of thinking, judgement and strategy are the most enjoyable	1	2	3	4	5
15.	I am interested in why people do the things they do.	1	2	3	4	5
16.	I feel alive when I come in contact with nature	1	2	3	4	5
17.	I am good at solving visual puzzles	1	2	3	4	5
18.	I have always dreamed of being a musician or singer, or working with them	1	2	3	4	5
19.	I love to use lots of different words to express myself	1	2	3	4	5
20.	I easily notice when music sounds off-key or wrong	1	2	3	4	5
21.	I can easily imagine how an object would look from another perspective	1	2	3	4	5
22.	I enjoy debates and discussions	1	2	3	4	5

continued on the next page...

#	Statement	Scale	a	b	c	d	e	f	g	h
23.	I often seem to think more clearly when I walk or run	1 2 3 4 5	■	■	■	□	■	■	■	■
24.	I find it easy to mix with new and different types of people	1 2 3 4 5	■	■	■	■	■	□	■	■
25.	I have interests or hobbies that I don't talk much about	1 2 3 4 5	■	■	■	■	■	■	□	■
26.	I much prefer activities that use my hands (crafts/mechanics) or body (sports/dance/movement)	1 2 3 4 5	■	■	■	□	■	■	■	■
27.	I usually sort out arguments between friends	1 2 3 4 5	■	■	■	■	■	□	■	■
28.	I know things better if I can touch and examine them directly	1 2 3 4 5	■	■	■	□	■	■	■	■
29.	I can find my way around in unfamiliar places	1 2 3 4 5	■	■	■	■	□	■	■	■
30.	I enjoy individual sports/activities best	1 2 3 4 5	■	■	■	■	■	■	□	■
31.	I always think through a problem carefully, considering all the consequences	1 2 3 4 5	■	□	■	■	■	■	■	■
32.	I find it easy to remember quotes or famous sayings	1 2 3 4 5	□	■	■	■	■	■	■	■
33.	I like messing around with something to figure out how it works	1 2 3 4 5	■	■	■	□	■	■	■	■
34.	I like having pets / I love animals	1 2 3 4 5	■	■	■	■	■	■	■	□
35.	I like working and thinking on my own and quietly	1 2 3 4 5	■	■	■	■	■	■	□	■
36.	I enjoy word games, and like nonsense rhymes, puns and tongue twisters	1 2 3 4 5	□	■	■	■	■	■	■	■
37.	I like outside activities such as gardening or nature walks	1 2 3 4 5	■	■	■	■	■	■	■	□
38.	I find ball games easy and enjoyable	1 2 3 4 5	■	■	■	□	■	■	■	■
39.	I always like to know how things work	1 2 3 4 5	■	□	■	■	■	■	■	■
40.	I know my personal strengths and weaknesses well because I think about them often	1 2 3 4 5	■	■	■	■	■	■	□	■
41.	I love to classify things and know the small details about whatever interests me	1 2 3 4 5	■	■	■	■	■	■	■	□
42.	I always look for a rational explanation for things	1 2 3 4 5	■	□	■	■	■	■	■	■
43.	I always know how I am feeling	1 2 3 4 5	■	■	■	■	■	■	□	■
44.	I have always felt drawn to the world of nature, of animals, plants, birds etc.	1 2 3 4 5	■	■	■	■	■	■	■	□
45.	My friends always come to me for emotional support and advice	1 2 3 4 5	■	■	■	■	■	□	■	■
46.	I am good at drawing	1 2 3 4 5	■	■	■	■	□	■	■	■
47.	If someone is hurt or upset, I always help them by just talking with them	1 2 3 4 5	■	■	■	■	■	□	■	■
48.	I like numbers and am good at arithmetic	1 2 3 4 5	■	□	■	■	■	■	■	■

Totals:

- a — Linguistic-Verbal
- b — Logical-Mathematical
- c — Musical
- d — Bodily-Kinesthetic
- e — Spatial
- f — Interpersonal
- g — Intrapersonal
- h — Naturalist

This quiz can be taken online in the **Multiple Intelligence App** in the **Self-Assessment** tab of your **Reach⁺** Career File

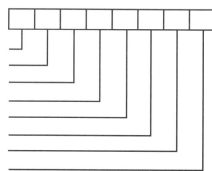

My Intelligences

Mark on the table below the results for each of your intelligences. Then join up the marks to form your Multiple Intelligence Profile.

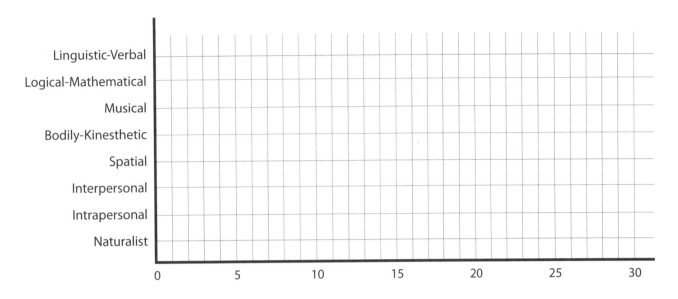

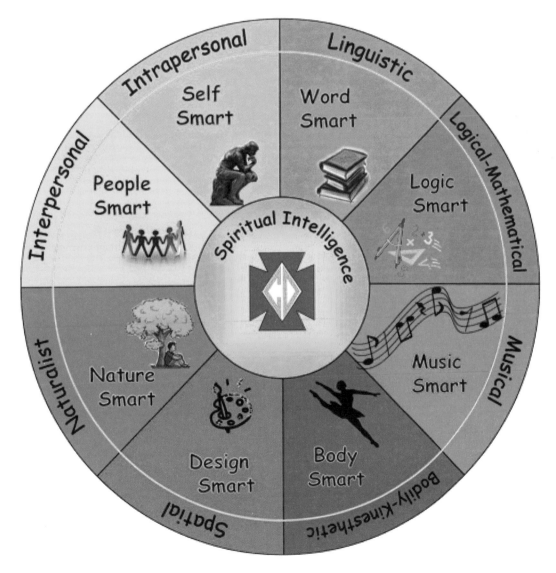

Next, read through the brief descriptions of each of the intelligences that follows.

Linguistic-Verbal

People with linguistic intelligence have well-developed verbal skills and sensitivity to the sounds and meanings of words.

What It Means?

Linguistic intelligence means to have a deep understanding and appreciation of words and the use of language. It is the most widely shared human competence, and is used particularly in the work of poets, nvelists, journalists, and public speakers).

Young adults with this kind of intelligence enjoy writing, reading, taking notes, researching, telling stories, or doing linguistic puzzles like word searches or crosswords.

Famous People:

William Shakespeare and *J.K. Rowling* are famous examples of linguistically intelligent people.

Related Careers:
- Librarian
- Speech and Language Therapist
- Radio or TV Presenter
- Blogger
- Curator
- Journalist
- Legal Assistant
- Lawyer
- Secretary
- Writer (TV series, games, reviews)
- Typist
- Proofreader
- Language Teacher
- Politician
- Public Speaker
- Talk-show Host
- Editor

Logical-Mathematical

Logical-mathematical intelligence is the ability to calculate, quantify and handle logical thinking and problem solving.

What It Means?

Logical intelligence is an ability to understand numbers and concepts well, and to have excellent reasoning skills. This is usually well developed in mathematicians, scientists, programmers, and detectives.

Young adults with lots of logical intelligence are interested in patterns and they are drawn to mathematical problems, brainstorming, investigating, computers, and programming.

Famous People:

Bill Gates, *Albert Einstein* and *Marie Curie* are famous examples of logically intelligent people.

Related Careers:
- Computer Programmer
- Accountant
- Engineer
- Scientist or a Science Teacher
- Mathematician
- Auditor
- Purchasing Agent
- Underwriter
- Statistician
- Actuary
- Technician
- Economist
- Bookkeeper

Musical

Musical intelligence is the ability to tell the difference between pitch, rhythm and tone.

What It Means?

This intelligence enables us to recognise, create, reproduce, and reflect on music, as demonstrated by composers, conductors, musicians, vocalists, and sensitive listeners.

Interestingly, there is often a connection between music and emotions. Additionally, **mathematical and musical intelligences are said to share common thinking processes**.

Young adults with this kind of intelligence are usually quite aware of sounds others miss, and enjoy listening to music, singing, repeating, harmonising, dubbing, rapping, multimedia presentations, drumming to themselves, creating music, and going to concerts.

Related Careers:
- Disc Jockey (D.J.)
- Musician
- Instrument Maker
- Piano Tuner
- Music Therapist
- Songwriter
- Conductor
- Singer
- Music Teacher
- Voice Actor/Actress
- Instrument Salesperson
- Music Critic
- Composer

Famous People:

Lady Gaga, *Ed Sheeran,* and *Beethoven* are famous examples of musically intelligent people.

Bodily-Kinesthetic

Bodily-Kinesthetic intelligent people have excellent coordination, balance, dexterity, strength, fine motor skills, speed, flexibility, and use their entire body to relate thoughts and feelings.

What It Means?

This intelligence involves a sense of timing and the perfection of skills through mind-body union. Athletes, dancers, painters, performers, surgeons, and craftspeople exhibit well-developed bodily kinesthetic intelligence.

Young adults with this intelligence usually enjoy performing, football, dancing, making or constructing things, crafts, fashion, shapes, exercise, and gymnastics.

Related Careers:
- Physical Therapist
- Recreational Worker
- Dancer
- Actor
- Farmer
- Mechanic
- Carpenter
- Craftsperson
- Physical Education Teacher
- Factory Worker
- Jeweller
- Athlete
- Mime
- Artistic Painter
- Surgeon

Famous People:

Brian O'Driscoll, Serena Williams and *Jennifer Lawrence* are examples of people with this intelligence.

Spatial

Spatial intelligence is the ability to think in three dimensions.

What It Means?

Having these skills means you have the ability to think in images, have very good graphic and artistic potential, and an active imagination. Graphic artists, architects, and map-makers, sailors, pilots, sculptors, painters are examples of spatially intelligent jobs.

Young adults with this kind of intelligence may be fascinated by mazes or jigsaw puzzles and spend free time drawing. They tend to be good at reading maps, playing chess, drawing diagrams and illustrations, repairing machinery and understanding geometry.

Famous People:

Leonardo da Vinci, *Amelia Earhart* and *Andy Warhol* are examples of famous spatially intelligent people.

Related Careers:
- Pilot
- Engineer
- Hunter
- Web Designer
- Surveyor
- Architect
- Urban Planner
- Graphic Artist
- Interior Decorator
- Photographer
- Art teacher
- Inventor
- Fine Artist
- Sculptor
- Guide

Interpersonal

Interpersonal intelligence is the ability to understand and interact very well with others.

What It Means?

It involves excellent verbal and non-verbal communication skills, being sensitive to the moods and temperaments of others, and the ability to consider different perspectives on a situation. Those who have highly developed interpersonal intelligence may become successful leaders, bosses, agents, and public speakers.

Young adults with this kind of intelligence are leaders among their peers, are good at communicating, and seem to understand others' feelings and motives. Teachers, social sorkers, actors, and politicians are careers that require interpersonal intelligence.

Famous People:

Oprah Winfrey, Mary McAleese and *Barack Obama* are all well known people with interpersonal intelligence.

Related Careers:
- Administrator
- Manager
- School Principal
- Personnel Worker
- Arbitrator
- Sociologist
- Anthropologist
- Counselor
- Psychologist
- Nurse
- Public Relations Worker
- Travel Agent
- Social Director

Intrapersonal

Intrapersonal intelligence is the capacity to understand yourself, your thoughts and feelings, and to use this knowledge to plan and reflect on your life.

What It Means?

People with intrapersonal intelligence know themselves well: their dreams, goals, moods, strengths, and limits. This intelligence is evident in psychologists, spiritual leaders, and philosophers.

These young adults may appear shy and are very aware of their own feelings, are self-motivated and make decisions based on what is right for them. Some enjoy keeping a diary.

Related Careers:
- Psychologist
- Clergy
- Psychology Teacher
- Therapist
- Counsellor
- Theologian
- Entrepreneur

Famous People:

Sigmeund Freud, *James Joyce* and *Anne Frank* are all famous people with intrapersonal intelligence.

Naturalist

The Naturalist is sensitive towards nature and the world around them.

What It Means?

People with this intelligence were clearly of value in our evolutionary past as hunters, gatherers, and farmers. They have the ability to observe patterns in nature, have a love of being outdoors and are very interested in the well-being of the environment. This type of intelligence is important in botanists and chefs, as well as any outdoors work.

Young people with this intelligence usually enjoy camping, gardening, hiking and exploring the outdoors. They are interested in growing plants, taking care of animals and studying nature with binoculars, telescopes and microscopes.

Related Careers:
- Astronomer
- Botanist
- Wildlife Illustrator
- Meteorologist
- Chef
- Geologist
- Landscape Architect
- Conservationist
- Gardener
- Ornithologist
- Beachcomber
- Zoologist

Famous People:

Charles Darwin, *Jane Goodall* and *Bear Grylls* are examples of famous people with naturalist intelligence.

Exercise: My Intelligences Reflection

1   After reading the descriptions of the intelligences and reviewing your scores, which three intelligences do you feel are your strongest?

_____

_____

_____

2   Discuss the main reasons you believe that these intelligences are your strongest.

_____

_____

_____

_____

_____

_____

_____

_____

3   Discuss whether or not you think it would be important to consider your intelligences when choosing a career path. Include your thoughts on how any of your current career ideas may benefit or may not from your intelligences.

_____

_____

_____

_____

_____

_____

_____

_____

_____

_____

_____

_____

_____

_____

Career Skills

Exercise: Skills for the Job

A local recruitment agency is selecting candidates for several positions in a variety of businesses. There have been a large number of applicants for each position, and after dismissing all the candidates who do not have enough qualifications for the jobs, there still remain far more applications than there are jobs available.

The Human Resources manager in your agency has asked for your help with narrowing down the applicants, by identifying the most important 'transferable skills' for each job. Based on your choices, applicants will be re-evaluated for the positions.

#1. Select a Business

The business areas and the positions they are recruiting for are listed below. Split into groups of four, take one business area from the list, and on the following page enter that business area and the four job roles across the top.

Business Area:	Job 1	Job 2	Job 3	Job 4
Band:	Keyboard Player	Song Writer	Tour Manager	Sound Engineer
Construction:	Architect	Site Foreman	Carpenter	Accountant
Football Team:	Coach	Physio-therapist	Manager	Player
Hairdressing Salon:	Trainee Hairdresser	Senior Stylist	Salon Receptionist	Beauty Therapist
Hospital:	Surgeon	Nurse	Pharmacist	Administrator
Hotel:	Receptionist	Bar Manager	Marketing Manager	Conference Manager
Restaurant:	Head Chef	Restaurant Manager	Waiter	Commis Chef
Secondary School:	Principal	Secretary	English Teacher	Guidance Counsellor
Supermarket:	Store Manager	Stores Assistant	Till Operator	Marketing Manager
Airline:	Pilot	Flight Attendant	Mechanical Engineer	Book-in Agent

#2. Top five skills for the job

Most skills are needed by all job roles, but some are especially important in certain roles. Your group's task is to find the **five most important skills** for each of the four job roles in the business area you have chosen, and to justify those choices. First, read through the Career Skills Definitions, and tick off the five skills which you believe are the most necessary for each job in your business area.

Job Roles Worksheet

Business Area:

	Job 1	Job 2	Job 3	Job 4
Enter occupation titles here: (e.g. pilot, surgeon, etc...)				

PEOPLE SKILLS

Sensitivity to others				
Insight into others				
Openness				
Respect				
Speaking / Presenting				
Active listening				
Conversation				
Persuasion				
Team membership				
Team participation				
Leadership				

TASK SKILLS

Planning / Organising				
Time management				
Practical skills				
Computer skills				
Problem solving				
Business awareness				
Customer focus				

PERSONAL SKILLS

Learning skills				
Adaptability				
Goal setting				
Initiative				
Independence				
Motivation				
Dependability				
Professionalism				

Career Skill Definitions

PEOPLE SKILLS	
Sensitivity to others	*Shows ability to maintain a deep interest in the concerns and feelings of others. Inclined to find ways to help people.*
Insight into others	*Shows an understanding of what makes people do what they do, and tolerance of the actions of others. Good at reading the moods of others.*
Openness	*Is open to, and communicates with people at all levels. Inclined to share personal experiences and trust people.*
Respect	*Shows consideration for the feelings, needs, thoughts, wishes and preferences of others (including other cultures and races).*
Speaking / Presenting	*Presents information clearly and confidently to other individuals or groups. Maintains good eye contact and keeps the attention of an audience or individual.*
Active listening	*Pays full attention to what other people are saying, takes time to understand the points being made, asks questions as needed, and does not interrupt inappropriately.*
Conversation	*Speaks clearly and listens attentively. Attends to other people, not to themselves. Seeks clarification where necessary and attends to body language appropriately.*
Persuasion	*Shows ability to influence peoples beliefs and actions. Shows ability to win people's co-operation and support for ideas or activities.*
Team membership	*Works easily with groups of people and shows loyalty and commitment to the team's objectives. Attends to each member's views equally.*
Team participation	*Openly expresses views and opinions within a group. Shows willingness to take on tasks and responsibilities as appropriate to one's experience.*
Leadership	*Shows the ability to communicate a vision or goal to others and lead them towards achieving it. Pushes for action and results, and wins the support and help of others.*

TASK SKILLS	
Planning / Organising	*Creates clear goals, identifies and finds the resources (e.g. time, people, materials) needed to achieve them, and schedules tasks so that work is completed on time.*
Time management	*Takes the time to organise events and tasks carefully so as to use time efficiently. Uses a diary/planner to ensure tasks are undertaken.*
Practical skills	*Uses equipment, tools or technology effectively. Easily follows instructions and shows willingness to use whatever tools or technology is required.*
Computer skills	*Confidently uses a computer to write documents, browse the internet or use email programs. Can save files, locate them efficiently and print them.*
Problem solving	*Shows interest in finding the cause of problems, looks for and chooses effective solutions and takes the necessary action to resolve them.*
Business awareness	*Shows understanding of the main business activities of the company/organisation. Has a good sense of the business opportunities available and the primary competitors.*
Customer focus	*Shows understanding and concern for customers' needs, is helpful and friendly to them, and deals effectively with any questions or complaints they may have.*

PERSONAL SKILLS	
Learning skills	*Seeks and willingly takes opportunities to learn. Shows interest in personal learning and development. Looks for feedback to improve understanding.*
Adaptability	*Adapts easily to new challenges and shows openness to new ways of doing things. Effective at changing plans or actions to deal with changing situations.*
Goal setting	*Shows the ability to make a decision about what is wanted and determines when it is to be achieved. Stays committed to the goal, and deals with setbacks realistically.*
Initiative	*Demonstrates ability to take the initiative in a situation. Shows inclination to find opportunities to make decisions or influence events.*
Independence	*Able to perform tasks effectively with minimum help or approval, or without direct supervision.*
Motivation	*Shows the drive to succeed and excel at tasks. Shows confidence in abilities and expects to succeed at all tasks agreed on.*
Dependability	*Is reliable, responsible and dependable in fulfilling duties. Carefully checks work to ensure all details have been considered.*
Professionalism	*Remains calm and self-controlled under stressful situations. Works to deliver the best interests of the organisation at all times, and maintains appropriate dress code.*

#3. Prepare for presentation

Each member of your group must now select one of the job roles, and prepare to present your group's findings to the recruitment agency. Fill in the following form with the five skills you would recommend and explain why you chose those skills.

Job Role:

First Skill: _____

Why it's important: _____

_____

_____

_____

Second Skill: _____

Why it's important: _____

_____

_____

_____

Third Skill: _____

Why it's important: _____

_____

_____

_____

Fourth Skill: _____

Why it's important: _____

_____

_____

_____

Fifth Skill: _____

Why it's important: _____

_____

_____

_____

#4. Present your findings (optional)

Each group now nominates one member to make a presentation to the recruitment agency (your class). This member should give a short presentation mentioning the business type, one job role selected, the five skills chosen as most important for the position, and **why those skills were chosen**.

My Career Skills

You might be surprised to know that you already have many of the skills which are essential for employment in the modern workplace. These are not the specific knowledge based skills you would learn during an apprenticeship, in college or at work, but the *'transferable skills'* which we all need to use when we work with other people, on projects or even by ourselves. You develop these skills simply from being involved in everyday activities. They are not formally 'taught' in school, but they may develop there, at home, or through your hobbies, activities, and friendships.

The skills we are talking about are quite ordinary, that's why we don't usually notice them. These 'ordinary' skills are so taken for granted that we seldom make any effort to improve or develop them. Terms such as 'communication skills', 'people skills' and 'organisation skills' are just some of the many skills which most people develop without even knowing about it.

Why are they important?

Lets put it this way. Two equally qualified people have applied for a job as a scientist. At the job interview, each is asked if they think that they would be good at the job. The first person answers with a simple "yes", the second one also answers "yes", and continues to discuss why they think they would be good. Both are well qualified for the job, but the second candidate has better 'communication skills', i.e. is simply better able to communicate when asked for information. Both may have honours degrees; but the better developed 'ordinary' skill of communication gives the edge to the second candidate.

Chances are, the first candidate thought that having the right qualification was all that was needed to get the job. Big mistake! It's safe to assume that for every job you apply for, there will also be several others who will have the same or better qualifications. So it is not necessarily the qualifications that win the job contract! More often, it is the 'ordinary' skills, and the evidence that you have developed them that counts.

Where do I start?

You can use the exercise on this worksheet to discover the most sought after skills needed to get jobs in the modern workplace. By rating yourself on these skills, you can see where your strengths and weaknesses may lie. Then, you can look for opportunities to develop and practice your underdeveloped skills so that regardless of your academic achievements, you will be able to show others just how skillful you are.

Exercise: Career Skills Self-Assessment

While doing this exercise, consider all of your experience to date. Take note of the activities and responsibilities that are a normal part of your school, college, or work life; your hobbies, involvement in sports, and even your family life. Involvement in any of these activities offers the opportunity to develop many of the skills detailed below, even if only in a small way. After completing this self-assessment exercise, complete the Summary and Action Plan on the last page of this worksheet.

Well Developed
I show this skill often, and others know I can be relied upon to use this skill effectively when needed.

Some Experience
I have had opportunity to develop this skill and have used it in a work, home, or school/college environment in a small way.

Undeveloped
I have not had the opportunity to develop this, or have not taken opportunities to develop this.

PEOPLE SKILLS

Sensitivity to others
Ability to maintain a deep interest in the concerns and feeling of others. Inclined to find ways to help people.

Insight into others
Has developed an understanding of what makes people do what they do, and is tolerant of the actions of others. Good at reading the moods of others.

Openness
Is open to, and encourages communication with all people at all levels. Inclined to share personal experiences and trust people.

Respect
Takes the feelings, needs, thoughts, wishes and preferences of others (including other cultures and races) into consideration, and gives them worth and value.

Speaking
Can present information clearly and confidently to other individuals and groups. Maintains good eye contact and can keep the attention of an audience or individual.

Active listening
Gives full attention to what other people are saying, takes time to understand the points being made, asks questions as needed, and does not interrupt inappropriately.

Conversation
Speaks clearly and listens attentively. Attends to the other person, not to oneself. Seeks clarification where necessary and attends to body language appropriately.

Persuasion
Shows ability to influence peoples beliefs and actions. Easily wins people's co-operation and support for ideas or activities.

Team membership
Works easily with groups of people and shows loyalty and commitment to the team's objectives. Attends to each member's views equally.

Team participation
Openly expresses views and opinions within a group. Shows willingness to take on tasks and responsibilities as appropriate to one's experience.

Leadership
Has the ability to communicate a vision or goal to others and lead them towards achieving it. Pushes for action and results, and wins the support and help of others.

TASK SKILLS

Planning
Creates clear goals, identifies and finds the resources (e.g. time, people, materials) needed to achieve them, and schedules tasks so that work is completed on time.

Time management
Takes the time to organise events and tasks carefully so as to use time efficiently. Uses a diary/planner to ensure tasks are undertaken.

Practical
Uses equipment, tools or technology effectively. Easily follows instructions and shows willingness to use whatever tools or technology is required.

Computing
Confidently uses a computer to write documents, browse the internet and use email programs. Can save files, locate them efficiently and print them.

Problem solving
Seeks to find the cause of problems, find and choose effective solutions and take the necessary action to resolve them.

Business awareness
Understands the main business activities of a company/organisation. Has a good sense of the business opportunities available, and the primary competitors.

Customer focus
Shows understanding and concern for customers needs, is helpful and friendly to them, and deals with any questions or complaints they may have.

PERSONAL SKILLS

Learning
Seeks and willingly takes opportunities to learn. Shows interest in personal learning and development. Looks for feedback to improve understanding.

Adaptability
Adapts easily to new challenges and is open to new ways of doing things. Effective at changing plans or actions to deal with changing situations.

Goal setting
Ability to make a decision about what is wanted, and determine when it is to be achieved. Stays committed to the goal, and deals with setbacks realistically.

Initiative
Takes the initiative to improve a situation. Seeks opportunities to influence events, or make decisions.

Independence
Able to perform tasks effectively with minimum help or approval, or without direct supervision.

Achievement motivation
Has the drive to succeed and excel at tasks. Strives to exceed expectations. Shows confidence in abilities and expects to succeed at all tasks agreed on.

Dependability
Is reliable, responsible and dependable in fulfilling duties. Carefully checks work to ensure all details have been considered.

Professionalism
Remains calm and self-controlled under stressful situations. Works to deliver the best interests of the organisation at all times, and maintains appropriate dress code.

Exercise: Career Skills Summary and Action Plan

Now that you are familiar with some of the most important transferable skills $\boxed{+ \mid \text{add to } \textbf{Career Portfolio}}$ desired by employers, it is a good idea to take note of those you have developed the most. These will be some of the things you would mention when writing your CV, along with some examples of how they were developed or used. You can also use this information when preparing for a job interview.

An employer will be looking to see what skills you have, and for evidence of how you have actually applied them. They won't accept that you have them just because you say so. Fill in the section below to summarise your most developed skills.

MOST DEVELOPED SKILLS

Comments: *(e.g. how I developed this, where I used it)*

1.

2.

3.

What about those skills you have not yet been able to develop? These could be the very things that could go against you when looking for a job. Remember, most employers want just about all of the skills mentioned in this exercise, and they may well ask you if you have had any experience of using such skills. So why not set targets for developing some of your weaker skills? Start by listing three of the skills you would like to get more experience with, and then note some of the activities you could become involved in to help develop them. Ask for suggestions from friends and advisors if you can't think of activities yourself.

SKILLS TO DEVELOP

Comments: *(e.g. what activities can I get involved in to develop this)*

1.

2.

3.

Enterprise Skills

In previous generations, only a few people needed to be enterprising such as certain business people, managers and those who were disadvantaged and had to struggle to survive. The rest of the population needed little initiative, flexibility or resourcefulness in order to make a living. The most important requirement for the vast majority was to follow instructions and persevere when things were tough.

Today, however, everyone needs enterprise. In fact, enterprise is the key factor in influencing the success of an individual, an organisation, or indeed a nation. Schools and colleges are looking at ways to develop enterprise in order to allow their students to become more motivated and independent learners.

Why do we need enterprise capability?

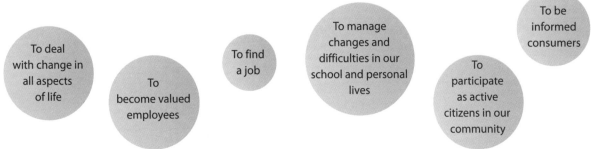

To deal with change in all aspects of life

To become valued employees

To find a job

To manage changes and difficulties in our school and personal lives

To participate as active citizens in our community

To be informed consumers

Being enterprising could mean starting up your own business – but it can also mean being creative with your work, risk taking, or generally doing things differently and making things happen.

What is enterprise?

There is a wide range of definitions on what enterprise is and what it means to be enterprising. The map below gives a snapshot of some of the characteristics of enterprising people:

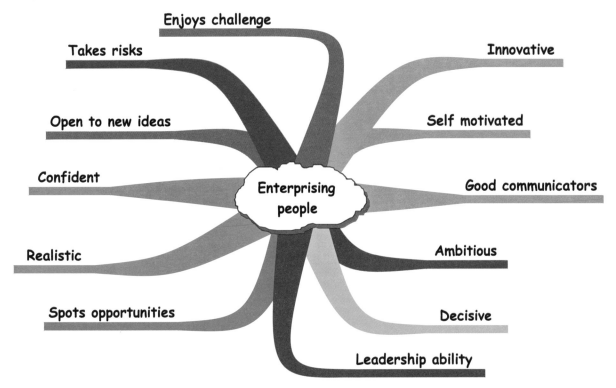

Enjoys challenge

Takes risks

Innovative

Open to new ideas

Self motivated

Confident

Enterprising people

Good communicators

Realistic

Ambitious

Spots opportunities

Decisive

Leadership ability

Anyone can develop these enterprising skills. Young people do so by going on work experience; taking part in enterprise activities at school; working towards the Young Enterprise Awards; participating in a school sports team; getting a part time job; organising an event or trip.

Exercise: Enterprise Skills Self Assessment

While doing the following exercise, you may need to think about the way you approach your work or tasks in general. For some statements below you may also need to think about how you are when undertaking a project you are interested in with other people. There are three parts to this exercise:

a) Read through the items and place a circle around the response you agree with most (complete this first).

b) In the right hand columns, enter the value you circled into the blank space for each of the 24 answers.

c) Add up the values in each column to find the score for each of the six categories

| + | add to **Career Portfolio** |

Rarely True / Seldom True / Sometimes True / Mostly True

#	Statement	Rarely True	Seldom True	Sometimes True	Mostly True
1.	I make changes to how things are done in order to prevent problems re-occurring	0	1	3	5
2.	I notice both the strengths and weaknesses of new ideas	0	1	3	5
3.	Instead of 'working on a hunch', I would use surveys and other such methods to gather information	0	1	3	5
4.	I am good at finding out the real cost of things, including the money, time, transport costs, etc.	0	1	3	5
5.	I work out 'best case' and 'worst case' scenarios for opportunities in my head	0	1	3	5
6.	I know when more information is needed	0	1	3	5
7.	I take time to figure out the effort involved in a project	0	1	3	5
8.	I am careful and keep a record of all materials and resources used	0	1	3	5
9.	I listen carefully even to 'crazy' ideas	0	1	3	5
10.	I prefer to find a number of solutions to a problem before taking action	0	1	3	5
11.	I often notice ways that people can improve a business or product I come in contact with	0	1	3	5
12.	I am good at knowing where to find what I need for a project or activity I undertake	0	1	3	5
13.	I consider all resources needed for an undertaking; including materials, technology, people, and money	0	1	3	5
14.	I do research to check whether my plans are realistic	0	1	3	5
15.	I tend to know whether information is essential or not and drop what's not useful quickly	0	1	3	5
16.	I look to find out how a task is coming along at regular intervals	0	1	3	5
17.	I often ask if there is another way of doing something	0	1	3	5
18.	I tend to see gaps where needs and wants are not met	0	1	3	5
19.	I often ask 'what if' questions	0	1	3	5
20.	I tend to anticipate problems and take action in time	0	1	3	5
21.	I think about what could go wrong and what the fallout could be	0	1	3	5
22.	I want to know more about other people's ideas before I take action.	0	1	3	5
23.	I seek advice on what and how much risk to take	0	1	3	5
24.	I check to make sure crucial information is accurate before acting on it	0	1	3	5

| Op | Id | Ri | In | Re | Pr |

My Enterprise Profile

Your enterprise profile is based on six key skills that characterise enterprising individuals. Fill in your results from the previous page in the box below and then plot them on the RADAR diagram.

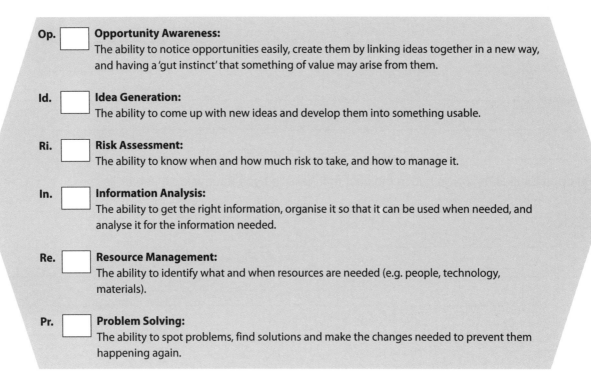

Op. ☐ **Opportunity Awareness:**
The ability to notice opportunities easily, create them by linking ideas together in a new way, and having a 'gut instinct' that something of value may arise from them.

Id. ☐ **Idea Generation:**
The ability to come up with new ideas and develop them into something usable.

Ri. ☐ **Risk Assessment:**
The ability to know when and how much risk to take, and how to manage it.

In. ☐ **Information Analysis:**
The ability to get the right information, organise it so that it can be used when needed, and analyse it for the information needed.

Re. ☐ **Resource Management:**
The ability to identify what and when resources are needed (e.g. people, technology, materials).

Pr. ☐ **Problem Solving:**
The ability to spot problems, find solutions and make the changes needed to prevent them happening again.

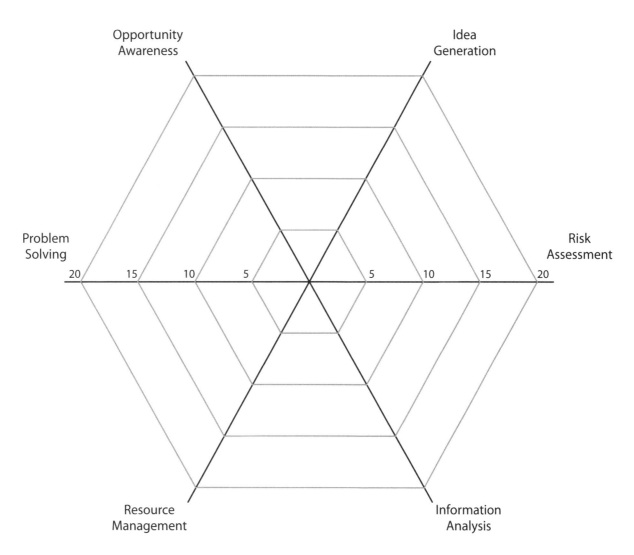

Exercise: Enterprise Skills Action Plan

If you were to get a job on leaving school, which enterprising skills would you be best able to offer your employer?

_____

_____

_____

_____

_____

What opportunities have you had in the past that have led you to develop these skills?

_____

_____

_____

_____

_____

_____

_____

Which enterprise skills would you most like to develop further and why?

_____

_____

_____

_____

_____

_____

_____

_____

_____

_____

_____

_____

Exercise: Who wants to be an Entrepreneur?

The following exercise asks you a number of questions about some of the typical characteristics found in entrepreneurs. Circle either **a**, **b**, or **c** based on how you would *actually* behave *right now*.

#1. Are You a Self-Starter?
a) If someone gets me started, I can keep going all right.
b) I do things my own way. Nobody needs to tell me to get going.
c) Easy does it. I don't get moving until I have to.

c	a	b

#2. How Do You Feel About Other People?
a) Most people bug me.
b) I like people. I can get along with just about anybody.
c) I have enough friends and I don't need anybody else.

a	c	b

#3. Can You Lead Others?
a) I can get people to do things if I drive them.
b) I can get most people to go along with me without much difficulty.
c) I usually let someone else get things moving.

c	a	b

#4. Can You Take Responsibility?
a) I'll take over if I have to, but I'd rather let someone else be responsible.
b) There's always some eager beaver around waiting to show off. I say, let them.
c) I like to take charge and see things through.

b	a	c

#5. How Good An Organiser Are You?
a) I like to have a plan before I start. I'm usually the one who lines things up.
b) I do all right unless things get too complicated. Then I may cop out.
c) I just take things as they come.

c	b	a

#6. How Good a Worker Are You?
a) I can't see that hard work gets you anywhere.
b) I'll work hard for a time, but when I've had enough, that's it.
c) I can keep going as long as necessary. I don't mind working hard.

a	b	c

#7. Can You Make Decisions?
a) I can if I have plenty of time. If I have to make up my mind fast, I usually regret it.
b) I can make up my mind in a hurry if necessary, and my decision is usually O.K.
c) I don't like to be the one who decides things. I'd probably blow it.

c	a	b

#8. Can People Trust What You Say?
a) I try to be on the level, but sometimes I just say what's easiest.
b) They sure can. I don't say things I don't mean.
c) What's the sweat if the other guy doesn't know the difference?

c	a	b

#9. Can You Stick With It?
a) If I make up my mind to do something, I don't let anything stop me.
b) If a job doesn't go right, I turn off. Why beat your brains out?
c) I usually finish what I start.

b	c	a

#10. Can You Keep Records?
a) Records are not important. I know what needs to be known without keeping records.
b) I can, but it's more important to get the work out than to shuffle numbers.
c) Since they are needed I'll keep records even though I don't want to.

a	b	c

Check what your score means on the next page...

Total circled in each column:

Multiply the total on the right by 10:

Multiply the total in the middle by 6:

Keep the total on the left:

Add these three for your Grand Total:

+ add to **Career Portfolio**

What your score means:

Score: 100

Excellent! *A perfect score. You are a born entrepreneur. You should definitely consider running your own business at some point in your life – the sooner the better. All you need is that brilliant idea, then you are on your way!*

Score: 91–99

Very good. *You definitely have what it takes to succeed in a business of your own. Get yourself the education you require to give you the knowledge you require to make it in the business world.*

Score: 72–90

Good. *You have the qualities of a successful entrepreneur with some weak areas. Look through those questions you scored low on – those in the left and middle columns of the score sheet. These are areas you need to develop your skills in before starting your own business. Of course, you could just employ or partner with someone who excels in those skills!*

Score: 40–71

So–so. *The prospect of your success in a business of your own is questionable. You have some deficiencies that might out-shadow some good traits you have. If you still want to go on with it, be sure to call up all the persistence you can get. However, you are going to face some tough work along the way.*

Score: 40 or less

Poor. *Being your own boss is not for you. You'd better keep your eye out for a comfortable and secure job. After all, why bother with all the risks and hassles of starting a business?*

Personal Statement

This personal statement exercise is an opportunity to practise the key skill of telling in writing, a future employer, university or college about your suitability for the job or course which you hope to study. If done well, it will demonstrate your enthusiasm and commitment, as well as your unique blend of talents and skills.

Doing this exercise is useful for the following reasons:

#1 You will learn the skill of promoting yourself in writing. It is likely that you will come across many application forms which request you to state your reasons for wanting a job, college place or PLC course over the next few years, so this experience will be something you can draw on.

#2 The exercise will force you to think through more clearly why you want a job or college course and how suitable it really is for you.

#3 If you are applying to UCAS, you will need to submit a personal statement as part of your application. These statements are reviewed and have an influence on who gets offered placements; so it is crucial that you make a strong personal statement if you are serious about your application.

#4 If you can express your attributes in writing, you will be better able to express them during interviews.

Points to Include

» Try aiming your statement at a particular employer or college in which you are interested. This will help you to focus your efforts, and it might be useful to have if you ever make an application to that institution. Is it a direct path to your chosen career?

» You may want to be a teacher and wish to study a degree in education. It is here that you might talk about your career aspirations. Why have you chosen to pursue this career? What has influenced your decision? Write about the subjects you want to study.

» Think about why this subject interests you and explain in detail. Show you have a good understanding of the course and that you have done your research, for example, you know what modules you will be studying, whether there are any work placements involved, the areas of the course you most look forward to studying and why.

» Why does the subject interest you? Are you already studying this subject, what do you enjoy about it, what skills have you learnt from it – essay writing, note taking, problem solving?

» You need to back up your interest by talking about what you have done to ensure this is the course for you. Have you read up on the profession, completed work experience, read additional text outside of the classroom? If so, include what you have learned.

Show examples of your personality

Few people are incredibly outgoing, have travelled the world, been captain of the football team and have completed a period of work experience in exactly the area suited to their future college course.

Be imaginative but honest about the things which you have experienced and how your interests or responsibilities may set you apart from other students. Try to be specific by providing detail or examples.

Think about what you have already achieved and experienced. The person reading your personal statement will see what kind of person you are and how you will fit in at their college or organisation.

- You may work part-time or have done 'work placement' as part of your TY, LCVP or LCA programme. Being punctual, balancing a part-time job with your studies and social life shows excellent time management skills.

- Work experience and project work that you have been actively involved in develops communication skills through working with different students and customers.

- You may have helped in a position of trust, handling cash or as a key-holder, being able to work with minimum supervision and use initiative. What activities do you do that help you gain these skills?

- Are you involved in any team sports? How often do you train? Do you hold any positions of responsibility? Would you like to continue this activity in college/work? If so, have you already looked into this?

- Are you a volunteer for a charity group or organisation? Do you help in your community? Have you travelled anywhere exciting? How has this influenced you?

- Do you have any plans for your summer break before going on to college or taking up your training place?

Reach+

Exercise: Personal Statement Preparation

Write a few statements about your interests and experience using the headings below. This will help provide a structure for your statement.

About the course - Why are you chosing it / how are you suitable / evidence of your interest

_____

_____

_____

_____

_____

_____

_____

_____

_____

Skills and Achievements - as related to going to college and as related to your course

_____

_____

_____

_____

_____

_____

_____

_____

Work Experience - particularily if relevent to your course(s), Future plans - what you hope for

_____

_____

_____

_____

_____

_____

_____

_____

Improving a Personal Statement

Before you begin your personal statement, read the following sample written by a student to support an application to study a University course in Physiotherapy. This is an early draft which needs improving:

I enjoy Biology and Chemistry subjects at school so much I have decided to pursue a course in Physiotherapy at degree level.

At University I look forward to studying a range of biology and physio topics. I am particularly interested in studying about sports injuries and visits to physio clinics to gain greater knowledge and skill.

As a member of the student council at my school I hold many responsibilities from organising and attending school functions, giving advice to junior members, to working effectively with other students very seriously. I have played keyboard in school musicals with the orchestra for the last five years and I have recently taken up piano lessons.

I am a keen sports player and I am a member of the school senior soccer and basketball teams. I have been part of the schools athletics squad over the last two years. I was nominated for "Sports Personality of the Year" award at the end of my first year in my school.

I have taught information technology skills to younger kids and I helped out a particular student to overcome language difficulties. I have organised sports days and Christmas parties for the elderly. I've have always loved watching science programmes on TV but my most memorable achievement was entering the Young Scientist of the Year competition. My project dealt with the effect heavy school bags are having on students posture and backs.

During my Transition year I got to attend a number of Career Open days and I carried out a lot of investagations into different paramedical careers. I got to know a lot about jobs in health (specifically physiotherapy and sports injuries).

Expert's Comments

Strong Points:

- Attempts to start with a reason for choosing this degree
- Presents an image of an active and well-rounded individual, not just academic
- Examples are provided about the prefect duties
- Valuable to include a reference to IT at some stage
- Assisting other people presents another aspect of the student's personality
- Being in a position of responsibility is useful to mention (i.e. A school prefect)
- Provides an image of a student with varied interests (e.g. Music and sports)
- Specific mention of Young Scientist project is good and it links to choice of course

Weak Points:

- A more insightful reason might be used to explain the choice of course
- Too many sentences begin the same way: they nearly all start with "I"
- Has not demonstrated any great understanding of the course or the career. What appeals to him about the profession?
- Did not mention the skills gained from participating in team sports
- Could be more concise about the science programmes watched and about how the 'Young Scientist' competition influenced his thinking
- No mention of the skills gained from having taken part in the competition
- No link to the degree is made at the end of the paragraph
- No concluding statement
- Could state what the student wants out of the degree
- Could mention which areas of science are of greatest interest
- Words such as 'a lot' are used twice in one sentence directly following another. Not clear if 'a lot' means extensive or challenging or comprehensive or none of these.
- Small number of spelling and grammar mistakes
- No mention of skills gained from being a school prefect
- The reference to Sports Personality of the Year in first year seems too long ago to be relevant given the more recent responsibilities and experiences
- At least some sentences should be linked. Almost all sentences are disconnected
- Has learning the piano really sold the student?

Tips for your statement

The following tips should help you write a Personal Statement which is easy to read and is professionally written. Follow the advice below to help you connect sentences and paragraphs together as well as help you vary the language you use.

Important Note:

- Remember - make sure your Personal Statement is your own work - colleges can identify if it is not!

In addition:
"*In addition* to my work experience I have gained valuable skills through voluntary work."

As well as:
"*As well as* my involvement in team games, I am also keen on playing individual competitive sport."

Reinforce:
"My involvement in the school voluntary programme has *reinforced* my decision to study a degree in Physiotherapy."

Strengthen:
"My decision to study a degree in Economics has been *strengthened* by my enjoyment and success studying it at school."

Furthermore:
"*Furthermore*, I am particularly suited to a degree in Chemistry because of my love for the subject and my keen interest to further my knowledge of the subject."

Not to mention
"Being involved in the voluntary work programme not to mention my work experience has provided an opportunity to work with a diverse range of people."

More recently:
"Although I have taken part in classical music concerts, more recently I have decided to learn to play the piano."

Enabled me:
"The opportunity to play in the school football team enabled me to work as part of a team."

Provided me:
"The work experience provided me with an opportunity to work with a range if people."

Opportunity to:
"The opportunity to work with people was provided by my work experience."

Advice about using "I"

Beginning too many sentences with "I" is very easy to do, especially when writing about yourself. Instead try to create varied sentences with a range of alternative starting points:

DON'T WRITE:	WRITE:
I am Captain of the Hockey Team...	*Being Captain of the Hockey team...*
I enjoy playing sport...	*Having enjoyed playing football ...*
I enjoy socialising...	*Socialising is important to me because...*
I have taken part in...	*Taking part in ...*
I have gained a number of skills...	*The skills I have gained from ...*

Write your statement out on the following pages with pencil. Erase your mistakes and improve on it as you go. It may be helpful to draft a mind map of your statement before you begin. When you are happy with how it reads, type it and save it into your career file online. Get someone to proof-read it before sending it to a college: typing errors will not be acceptable.

Exercise: My Personal Statement

My Personal Statement (continued)

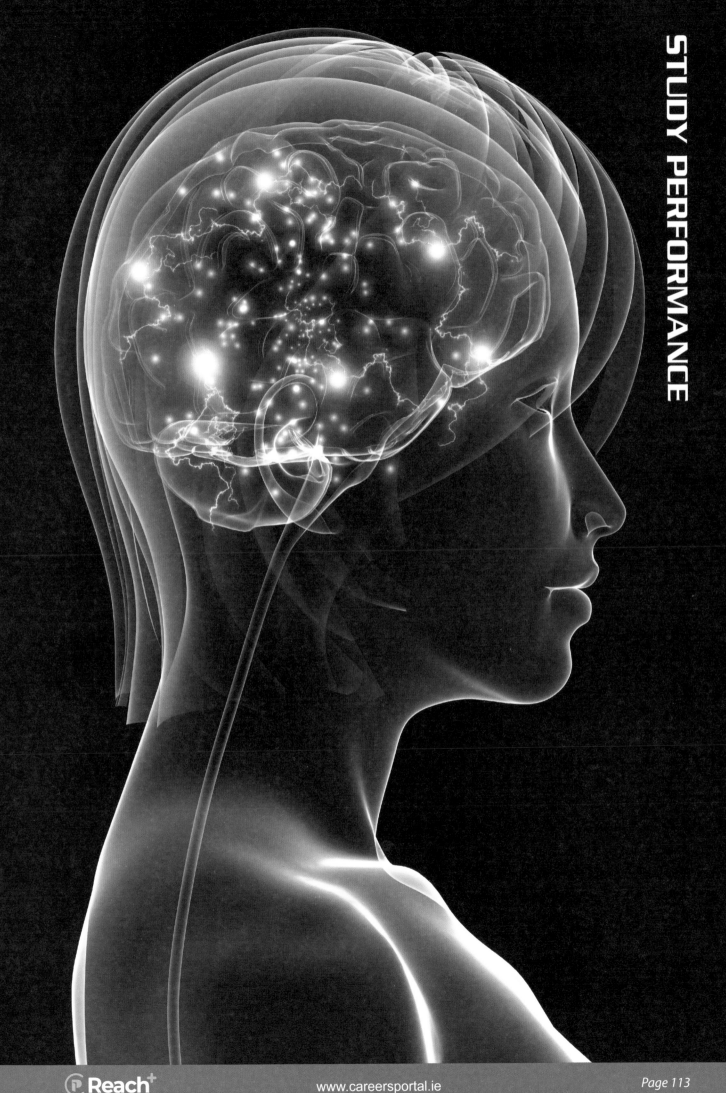

Learning Styles

When we start to learn something new, our first concern is understandably with the subject or content we are dealing with. But have you stopped to consider how you learn?

Educational experts have shown that by becoming more aware of how you learn, you can become a more efficient and effective learner. It has also been shown that there is no one single method of learning; there are many and what works best depends on the task, the situation and your personality. Psychologists tell us that we will be more effective learners if we are aware of the range of possible learning methods, know when to apply them, and know what works best for us.

What are Learning Styles?

Learning styles are typical ways in which people learn. There are, for example, different ways of taking in and receiving information. Some people pick up information better when they hear or discuss a topic (**auditory** learners). Others learn best through practical, hands-on activities (**tactile** learners) while others find visual information best (**visual** learners).

It is best to employ a combination of visual, auditory and tactile learning styles as much as possible. However, if one style works best for you, then developing this may help you learn more easily.

Advice for visual learning:
Use visual materials such as pictures, charts, and maps
Use colour to highlight texts and own notes
Take notes or use handouts; look carefully at headings and patterns of topics
Brainstorm using illustrations, mind maps and models
Use multi-media where possible (computers; mind maps)
Study in a quiet place away from visual disturbances
Visualise information as a picture
Skim-read to get an overview before reading in detail

Advice for auditory learning:
Participate frequently in class discussions and debates
Make speeches and presentations whenever possible
Read text out loud
Use your phone or mp3 player to record your ideas and/or notes and play them back as a form of revision
Create musical jingles and mnemonics to aid memory (see notes on note-taking skills)
Discuss your ideas verbally
Speak onto an audio-tape and listen to your own ideas played back

Advice for tactile / kinaesthetic learning:
Study in a comfortable position, not necessarily sitting in a chair
Stand up while working
Use flash cards, which you can shuffle frequently
Use touch, action, movement and hands-on learning wherever possible
Skim-read before reading in detail
Use bright colours to highlight reading material and turn it into posters or models
Move around to learn new things (read while you are using an exercise bike; model in clay to learn a new concept, learn off notes while walking around)

Along with receiving information in different ways, our brains can also manage the information in a number of different ways. Research has led psychologists* to identify four distinct styles or preferences that people use while learning. They suggest that most of us tend to follow only one or two of these styles, and that different learning activities may be better suited to particular styles. Knowing our predominant learning style can help us find ways to maximise our learning efficiency.

* Honey and Mumford.

Exercise: Learning Styles Quiz

There are three parts to the following exercise:

#1. Read through the items and place a circle around the response you agree with most.

#2. In the right hand columns, enter the value you circled into the blank space for each of the 32 answers.

#3. Add up the values in each column to find the score for each of the four categories.

		Strongly Disagree	Disagree	Neutral	Agree	Strongly Agree				
1.	I prefer learning by reading, listening and watching, than by doing	0	1	2	4	6				
2.	I like to know that what I learn comes from a credible source	0	1	2	4	6				
3.	I learn best when I believe in something or can relate to it personally	0	1	2	4	6				
4.	Often I do things just because I feel like it rather than thinking about it first	0	1	2	4	6				
5.	I believe that things should be done in a careful and logical manner	0	1	2	4	6				
6.	I tend to focus on the personal effects my decisions may have on others	0	1	2	4	6				
7.	I like to find out how and why things work	0	1	2	4	6				
8.	I tend to jump in and do things rather than plan things out in advance	0	1	2	4	6				
9.	To complete a task, I do whatever needs to be done	0	1	2	4	6				
10.	I easily get concerned with the feelings of others when working with them on tasks and projects	0	1	2	4	6				
11.	Often I can see more practical ways of doing things.	0	1	2	4	6				
12.	I am only happy when I have enough time to do a thorough and complete job	0	1	2	4	6				
13.	I enjoy following routines that are familiar to me	0	1	2	4	6				
14.	I think that what matters most about what you learn is whether it can be put into practice	0	1	2	4	6				
15.	I tend to make decisions carefully after weighing up all other possibilities first	0	1	2	4	6				
16.	Even when a decision seems right, I tend to think about the effects for a long time before I finally make up my mind	0	1	2	4	6				
17.	I get bored easily and prefer doing new things	0	1	2	4	6				
18.	I learn best from real-life experiences	0	1	2	4	6				
19.	I get stressed by having to stick to timetables or follow other peoples' schedules	0	1	2	4	6				
20.	I learn best when I am in a friendly environment	0	1	2	4	6				
21.	I like to take life as it comes and adapt to situations as required	0	1	2	4	6				
22.	I think things should be done properly, I suppose I could be seen as a bit of a perfectionist	0	1	2	4	6				
23.	Details bore me, I dislike double checking information for accuracy	0	1	2	4	6				
24.	I don't like taking things for granted, I like to check things out for myself	0	1	2	4	6				
25.	In discussions I put forward realistic ideas that I know will work	0	1	2	4	6				
26.	I only need to know the essentials, details slow me down	0	1	2	4	6				
27.	When discussing things I like to get straight to the point	0	1	2	4	6				
28.	I tend to look for or form theories about most things	0	1	2	4	6				
29.	I prefer to look at problems from as many different angles as I can before starting on them	0	1	2	4	6				
30.	I prefer working in a neat space where things are in their place	0	1	2	4	6				
31.	I get stressed by people who pressurise me to be more organised	0	1	2	4	6				
32.	I learn best by following simple step-by-step instructions	0	1	2	4	6				

Now add up the totals for each column in these boxes:

P	A	R	O

My Learning Style

Complete the graph below with the results from your Learning Style Exercise.

Today's Date: _____

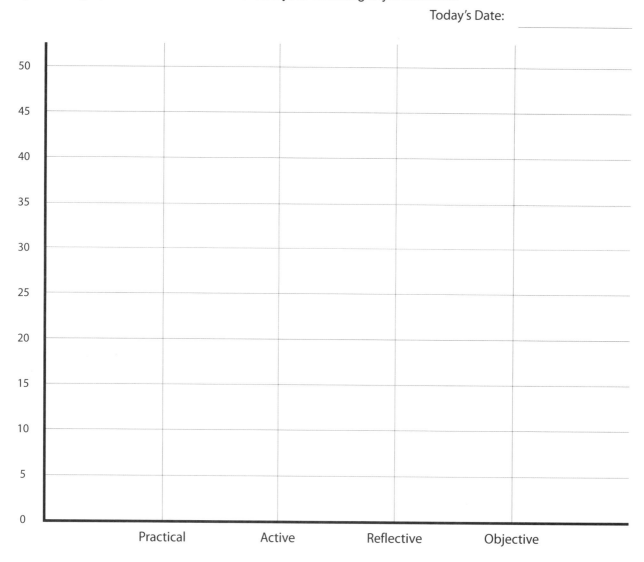

To find out what the general characteristics of the four styles are, read through the descriptions that follow. Most people can be characterised by their two strongest styles, for example:

Reflective + Active: Known for their strong people skills
Objective + Practical: Known for combining theory and application effectively
Practical + Active: Known for entrepreneurial skills

On the following pages, tick any boxes under the **Improving your learning** heading which you think you could **realistically** improve on. Discuss any changes you are considering making with your teachers first!

"Working life involves continuous learning – as each day will bring something new. Choosing a job role that fits with your strongest learning styles may make the role more natural for you".

Practical

Practical learners are keen on trying things out. They look for ideas that they can use to sort out problems they can see. They like to get on with things and tend to be impatient with open-ended discussions; they are practical, down-to-earth people.

Practical learners tend to be quite straightforward, saying what they mean, and can be blunt and to the point. They like order and like everything to have its place. They tend to be more organised than other types and find lists and schedules useful.

Natural Talents:

- Good with details
- Solving problems and getting results
- Focusing on a topic until it is completed
- Giving clear, well structured and detailed information

Have Difficulty with:

- Being innovative and considering alternatives
- Depending on others in a group
- Having to decide without enough information
- Visualising abstract things which can't be seen

Improving your learning:

- ☐ Create clear guidelines on how to handle each type of question which might appear in an exam.
- ☐ Choose a study area that is quiet and reasonably tidy.
- ☐ Write down any homework you receive clearly, as you may have difficulty following incomplete or unclear directions.
- ☐ Practise flexibility. You may prefer to do things the same way, but your school work will require you to find new ways of doing things.
- ☐ Try to find some relevance or use for what you're studying, to make it more meaningful for yourself.

Active

Active learners are people who learn by doing. They like to involve themselves in new experiences, and will 'try anything once'. They tend to act first and consider the consequences afterwards.

Active learners have a curious and investigative nature and like to invent new ways of solving problems. They like variety and change, but are inclined to get bored with seeing things through.

Natural Talents:

- Thinks of the possibilities and what 'could be'
- Not afraid to take risks or try the unknown
- Believes in firsthand experience – "doing is believing"
- Making quick, accurate decisions without all the facts

Have Difficulty with:

- Predictable and structured environments
- Blindly following others
- Fine tuning a project to completion
- Explaining how you arrived at your conclusion

Improving your learning:

- ☐ Read instructions and directions carefully and pay attention to the steps you take in coming to a conclusion or a decision. You will be examined on showing systematic, deductive thought processes, not just conclusions.
- ☐ Learn by 'doing' with a trial-and-error approach.
- ☐ Avoid procrastination and distractions – focus on the task at hand!
- ☐ When taking exams, choose abstract essay questions where possible.

Reflective

Reflective learners learn by observing and thinking about what happened. They like to consider all the possible angles and personal implications before coming to a considered opinion. They spend time listening and observing, and tend to be cautious and thoughtful.

Reflective learners look beyond the facts, data and details. They value relationships above all and learn best in a co-operative and friendly environment. They tend to have a talent for understanding human nature and reading the human side of cut-and-dry issues.

Natural Talents:

- Staying optimistic when others are negative
- Cooperating with others to achieve a goal
- Discussing the pros and cons of a situation with others
- Adapting to change, new situations and different people

Have Difficulty with:

- Remembering precise details and facts
- Keeping schedules and meeting deadlines
- Taking a lead in a group situation
- Focusing on the task at hand

Improving your learning:

- ☐ Find opportunities to study in a group.
- ☐ Ask for feedback from teachers, and learn to accept constructive criticism.
- ☐ Get in the habit of keeping a schedule and setting goals.
- ☐ Pay more attention to your teacher's content and less to their presentation skills.
- ☐ When writing, begin with a broad perspective and then narrow down to more detailed information.
- ☐ Learn to be more objective – take your feelings and opinions out of your work when necessary.
- ☐ Develop techniques to help you remember details.

Objective

Objective learners like to understand the theory behind actions. They prefer abstract concepts and facts in order to learn. They like to analyse things, and feel uncomfortable with opinions based on personal views.

Objective learners think problems through in a step by step way. Decisions are not made until the pros and cons are thought about and the facts established.

Natural Talents:

- Seeking objective truth
- Developing theories from information
- Researching and organising information
- Choosing words with care and attention

Have Difficulty with:

- Coming to a quick decision
- Reading emotional situations accurately
- Accepting others point of view
- Dealing with interruptions and changed priorities

Improving your learning:

- ☐ Ensure that you are familiar with all the questions which might appear on an exam: dealing with surprises may be challenging.
- ☐ Find a way to apply structure to otherwise vague questions in exams.
- ☐ Lay out your arguments logically and concisely.
- ☐ Find a balance between gathering information for a task, and actually doing the task.
- ☐ Make sure you have routine work completed before you forget it.

Exercise: Learning Strengths

+ add to **Career Portfolio**

#1. **a)** What type of learning do you prefer mostly, Visual, Auditory or Tactile?

_____

_____

_____

_____

_____

_____

_____

b) Give examples where your preferred type of learning was used and proved effective.

_____

_____

_____

_____

_____

_____

_____

_____

_____

#2. Using your test results and the descriptions of the four learning styles provided, describe...

a) Your top four learning talents:

1. _____

2. _____

3. _____

4. _____

b) The four things you have the most difficulty with:

1. _____

2. _____

3. _____

4. _____

c) Four ways you could improve your learning:

1. _____

2. _____

3. _____

4. _____

Learning Skills

1. Why Bother?

Many of you reading this are involved in a sport or a creative activity such as music, art or drama. Can you imagine what your chances of success in these fields would be if you didn't receive instruction on how to make changes and improvements to your performance? Sports people, musicians, writers, and actors are constantly looking at ways to make their performance better. Success in any of these fields of activity rarely happens without making adjustments and changes while practising or training.

Study is no different. As a first step in training yourself to get better at studying, it is well worthwhile taking time out to look critically and honestly at the precise way you go about studying and rate your study performance as it now stands.

Many successful companies also realise the importance of this approach in business and commit sizeable amounts of their budget to exploring ways that their workforce can be more efficient. This involves workers and managers working together and looking closely at how they go about their work. The improvement in 'work practice' results in people becoming more efficient and more productive workers. The business of doing the Leaving Cert is no different. You too can become a more productive student and increase your chances of getting what you want from school. But first lets find out ….

2. What do you want?

This section of the workbook is all about learning how you can use 'goal setting' to help you reach your potential. You will learn how to set and achieve goals and how to measure your progress in reaching them. You will explore what's holding you back and find ways to overcome obstacles.

The dictionary defines success as "accomplishing or completing a desire you want". It's all about your ability to want something bad enough (a goal) that you are willing to put in extra effort to reach. Success is not about walking through life hoping that something good happens to you. You ability to reach your goals begins by taking the following steps.

Action steps are like steps on a ladder. As you accomplish each one of the steps you are getting closer to your goal

a) Thinking about what you want to achieve and writing it down on paper.

b) Developing a plan to make it happen, backed up with specific study behaviours or action steps.

c) Reviewing your action steps to check what's working and what further adjustment you need to make to get closer to your goals.

This all sounds a bit exhausting, but once you set this plan in motion and begin to experience success you will even find the process of reaching for goals rewarding and satisfying.

Exercise: Setting and Resetting Targets

For the next available examination, write down what you want to achieve in the appropriate **Target** column for each subject. These are your target results for that period. Make sure that the target is achievable. Be realistic, set yourself up for success, and take into account your abilities and past performance. At the same time your goals for each subject should reflect your potential. Your targets should be grades you would be proud to achieve. Always try and stretch yourself.

When you get your results back from your teachers, write your scores under the **Actual** column for that term. Next, based on your performance to date, reset your targets for the next term. When you get your results, write them into the Actual column for that term, and so on. After each term, adjust your targets as you see fit, but never abandon the process of setting targets!

Exam Results Pre-Leaving Cert Year

Subjects	Level	Term Name: Grade		Term Name: Grade		Summer Grade	
		Target	Actual	Target	Actual	Target	Actual
English							
Irish							
Maths							
Total Points							

If you go to work on your goals, your goals will go to work on you. If you go to work on your plan, your plan will go to work on you. Whatever good things we build end up building us.
Jim Rohn

Exam Results Leaving Cert Year

Subjects	Level	Term Name: Grade		Term Name: Grade		Mocks Grade		Leaving Cert Grade	
		Target	Actual	Target	Actual	Target	Actual	Target	Actual
English									
Irish									
Maths									
Total Points									

Exercise: Study Skills & Study Behaviour

3. What are you doing?

So how do you go about study? In what way are your habits and behaviours helping or hindering you achieve your target results?

Go online and login to your **Reach⁺** account and select the **Study Performance** tab and take the Study Skills Questionnaire to find out. Be ruthlessly honest in the way you respond to questions. That way you'll get a realistic and truthful picture of your study performance.

Enter your results into the graph below.

Note: You can retake the questionnaire at a later time to review how much more effective and efficient you have become as a result of the changes you have made to the way you study.

| + | add to **Career Portfolio** |

Date: _____

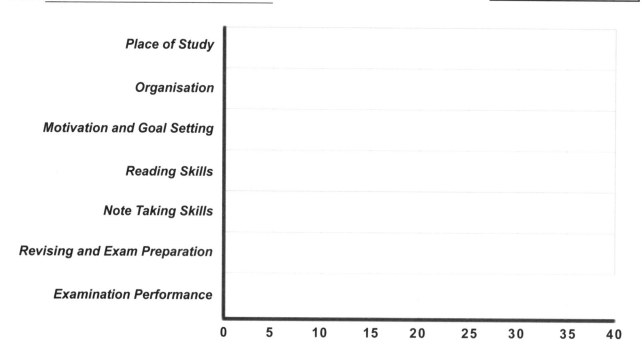

Graph categories (y-axis):
- Place of Study
- Organisation
- Motivation and Goal Setting
- Reading Skills
- Note Taking Skills
- Revising and Exam Preparation
- Examination Performance

x-axis: 0 5 10 15 20 25 30 35 40

4. Look at results of your study skills questionnaire.

Honestly ask yourself:

- When it comes to study, is what you are doing going to get you what you want?

- Are there issues concerning the way you go about study that need to change in order to help you get the result you want?

The seven worksheets that follow contain tips from students who had recently completed their Leaving Cert. Their tips can help you put some action steps in place that will bring you further up the ladder to reaching your goals. Read through the worksheets and you will become aware of aspects of your study behaviour that you may need to change. The worksheets may also alert you to the behaviours that you need to bin because these are the habits or behaviours that are holding you back.

#1. Place of Study

Tick any tips which you think might benefit you. Choose one of these which you can realistically improve on during the next term, and write it into your Study Behaviour Action Planner (p130).

☐ **I study by myself:** If possible do your study/school work in a room by yourself. Arrange with your parent/guardian that you have a place of study that is quiet and is separate from others in the house.

☐ **Not too hot, not too cold:** It is important that the temperature is comfortable in the room you study in. A room that is too warm or stuffy or too cold can have a big impact on your ability to concentrate.

☐ **There is good lighting on my desk:** A desk lamp is essential to avoid eye strain. Place your lamp on the opposite side to the hand that you write with. This way you will avoid shadows falling across your page.

☐ **I keep my desk free from clutter**: Ensure that your desk is tidy and free of clutter before you start a study session. Before you begin spend a couple of minutes organising your desk. You will be amazed how much better it makes you feel to work on a desk that is neat and free of clutter.

☐ **I actively discourage interruption:** Getting distracted by others can be very annoying and frustrating. Get the support of your parent or guardian on having your study place free from interruptions and noise. Turn off your mobile as soon as you start study.

☐ **I made sure the chair I sat at during study was suitable:** During study you need to sit for a long period of time. Make sure that your chair is as comfortable as possible.

☐ **Assign study times and let your friends know!:** It is important that you inform your friends, parents and family members of your study times. Arrange to text, phone or see friends outside study times. You will not lose friends by letting them know what you want!

☐ **There are no TV / Radio / Internet distractions:** Reduce or cut out distraction from TV and music during your study times. Research tells us that it is better for students to work without background music or radio. If this is difficult for you to forego then try rewarding yourself with them during study break times.

☐ **Have necessary resources to hand:** Always have the textbooks and equipment at hand that you are going to need for the study period.

☐ **I reserve my study desk for study and study only:** Never use your study desk for leisure activities such as listening to music. Get your brain to associate your place of study with study activity and nothing else.

#2. Being Organised

Tick any tips which you think might benefit you. Choose one of these which you can realistically improve on during the next term, and write it into your Study Behaviour Action Planner (p130).

☐ **I use a timetable:** It is vital that you draw up a timetable at the beginning of each week. Remember that the purpose of the timetable is to make your life easier. It will help you get more organised and take control, which in turn will result in less stress.

☐ **I include leisure time in my weekly timetable:** This will increase the chances of you sticking to the timetable you draw up.

☐ **I set myself precise learning goals:** It is strongly recommended that you spend time before you begin your study/homework session asking yourself 'what do I want to know at the end of working on this topic or question?'. Ask this for each topic/subject and write it down on a list before you start the session. Be as specific as possible on what you aim to know. This approach will give you focus and a sense of purpose.

☐ **I set time limits:** In your Leaving Cert examination you will be expected to work against the clock. Your study should also involve working against the clock. Allocate a set time for each study topic or question. Your teachers will be able to suggest how much time is reasonable to study any given question.

☐ **Prioritise:** Subjects taken at Higher Level demand more time and carry more Leaving Cert. points than subjects taken at Ordinary Level. The time you put into subjects taken at Honours Level should therefore be greater than the time given to your Ordinary Level subjects. Keep this in mind when drawing up your daily and weekly timetable.

☐ **I took frequent short breaks:** Educational Psychologists tell us that it is better to take frequent short breaks rather than infrequent long breaks. A 5-10 minute break every 40 minute is best for concentration and productive study. Try building this option into your timetable.

☐ **I learned how to relax and then focus:** Before beginning study each evening, perform a simple relaxation technique for about 10 minutes. This will help you stay concentrated on your work.

#3. Motivation & Goal Setting

First, ask yourself the following:

- What do you want from school?
- What do you want in terms of career or college?
- What will you need from school to go after the career/course/job you want?

The answers to these questions may not reveal themselves overnight. Students who have already been through the Leaving Cert have offered the following pointers as a way to get and stay motivated.

Tick any tips which you think might benefit you. Choose one of these which you can realistically improve on during the next term, and write it into your Study Behaviour Action Planner.

☐ **I made a written statement of what I wanted to achieve in my Leaving Cert:** Revisit the Setting Targets worksheet and be satisfied that you are happy with the target results you have set. Seek the advice of a teacher, parent, or your Guidance Counsellor when setting these targets. Writing down the targets I wanted to achieve made me focus more on what I really wanted.

☐ **Know what you want to do with your results:** If you are not sure, arrange an interview with your school Guidance Counsellor as early as possible. You can explore careers and college options by doing the following:

> Set 30/60 minutes aside each week to browse college literature or visit college web sites for information on courses and careers in further education.
>
> Attend College Open Days* and careers exhibitions during the year. Select the dates of 2/3 events that you will attend this year.
>
> Use the **Interest Profiler App** in the **Self-Assessment** tab of your **Reach⁺** Career File to explore the career and courses that match your interests.

☐ **I attended every class I could:** The more class time you miss the greater the risk of missing important learning points.

☐ **I cut out the part-time job:** It is hard to let go of the extra cash, but when you think about it, your job of studying will bring much greater returns in the long run.

☐ **Believe you have a bright future:** There are plenty of career and course opportunities for those taking their Leaving Certificate. I explored the alternative routes to getting my dream. I think it's very important to explore as many options as possible.

☐ **I looked after my health:** An obvious point, but it's easy to neglect your health as examinations approach. Psychology is now revealing links between physical and mental health. Your physical well-being has a huge impact on your ability to concentrate and relax when required.

* See College Open Days on page 31 for more information

#4. Reading Skills

Learning from Textbooks

Textbooks are basic tools in every student's learning. Efficient use of the textbook is therefore a very important study skill. There are ways of improving your reading so that you can understand and learn more.

One of the key points is to become more active and engaged with your textbook. Let's face it, textbooks are rarely exciting in themselves. The following proven method of using textbooks will improve your ability to learn. If you follow the method outlined below your textbook can become the most important tool at your disposal.

The **SQ3R** system is a reading method practiced by many students with good success. Read down through the descriptions and have a go at using this method the next time you use a textbook.

Tick any tips which you think might benefit you. Choose one of these which you can realistically improve on during the next term, and write it into your Study Behaviour Action Planner.

S ☐ SURVEY – the information necessary to focus more sharply on the material.

Spend a few moments browsing through the part of the book you are going to read. Take note of the way the author has organised the information. The headings and the sub-headings give you the best idea of the way the writer has arranged the key points. Be careful to note any diagrams, tables and maps there may be. Note the heading used and what is shown.

The purpose of this survey is to gather the information necessary in order to get focused and to decide what it is you are about to learn. This activity will help you formulate questions relating to the given subject.

Q ☐ QUESTION – come up with questions: Who? What? Where? When? Why? relating to what you are about to read.

One section at a time, turn the main headings into as many questions as you think will be answered in that section. The better the questions, the better your comprehension is likely to be. You may always add further questions as you proceed. When your mind is actively searching for answers to questions it becomes engaged in learning. So you will always be reading with the purpose of finding answers to the questions you have come up with.

R ☐ READ – fill in the information around the questions you have come up with.

You will have accomplished much of the first two steps in only a few moments and so the time you will spend on step 3 will be reduced. Only now do you actually read the words in the section. Read each section with your questions in mind. Look for the answers and notice if you need to make up some new questions. Note down your questions on paper.

R ☐ RECALL – test how much you can remember of what you just read.

After reading each section put the book to one side and try to recall the answers to the question you posed. Jot your points down in quick note form (see the note taking skills section). Look back again at the textbook (as often as necessary) and fill in any points you may have missed out on. Don't go on to the next section until you can answer those questions.

R ☐ REVIEW – reinforce what you have just learned.

When you are coming near to the end of your allocated time for this section of your study session, review all you have read. Go back over all the questions from all the sections in the textbook you covered during this session. See if you can still answer them. If not, look back on your notes and refresh your memory.

Reach+

#5. Note Taking Skills

Tick any tips which you think might benefit you. Choose one of these which you can realistically improve on during the next term, and write it into your Study Behaviour Action Planner.

☐ **I took notes as often as I could:** I took notes when reading material from textbooks and other sources for the first time. Whenever possible I took notes in class.

☐ **I kept my notes brief but informative:** I included information and not just headings in my notes but at the same time I kept my notes very brief. I'd advise that you only include enough key words or phrases that will bring the essential information/ideas to mind. Besides, one of the main reasons for taking notes is to save time, to allow more frequent revision. This won't happen unless your notes are brief and to the point.

☐ **I organised my notes for easy access:** I placed my notes into a ring binder folder. I was able to divide my folder up into different Subject Sections. I had a separate section to deal with notes that I was still working on. As soon as I finished taking notes on a given topic, I would transfer them into a Subject Section I had created. The ring binder folder is flexible and allowed me add notes to any topic from time to time.

Alternatively you could use a separate folder for each subject and a separate folder for notes currently under construction. This approach will allow you to combine notes from different sources. You can get an overview of the whole topic more clearly.

☐ **My class notes had main points only:** If you are taking notes in class, do not try to take everything down that the teacher says. Spend more time listening and try to take down the main points.

☐ **Make your notes legible and easy to use:** I discovered that it was very worthwhile making notes as clear and attractive as possible. The whole point in taking notes is that you refer to them often. As soon as I started to keep my notes in better shape I found it easy to refer back to them often. Up to then I had a tendency to clutter my notes. They must be easy and attractive to read. It is also a good idea to leave space to jot in additional notes later.

☐ **Watch for clues:** It is essential that you note the main points covered in the textbook chapter or class. Be alert for clues as to what the teacher thinks is important. One of the essential skills in note taking is being able to identify the key points in what you are listening to or reading.

☐ **Use your own words:** When taking notes I always tried to use my own words. You will remember your own phrases, sayings and expressions better. Don't use full sentences. Definitions are an exception to this rule.

☐ **Use visual cues and reminders:** As the brain can deal with information much more easily when it is presented in maps or graphs, it is a good idea to have your notes in this format as much as possible. Use mind maps if you find them helpful.

#6. Revising & Exam Preparation

Tick any tips which you think might benefit you. Choose one of these which you can realistically improve on during the next term, and write it into your Study Behaviour Action Planner.

☐ **I studied previous years exam papers:** Get to know how the course is laid out in the exam itself by studying past exam papers. Then put your time into the material that is important on the course. Learn from your examination of past papers how the marks are allocated.

☐ **I got to know in advance how much is expected:** Analyse past examination papers. Answer the questions in outline form. Jot down the *main ideas* and the *supporting ideas* for your answer. When you have completed the process, refer to your own notes. Fill out and change your notes as necessary. This process involves testing, recalling, and checking where the gaps or mistakes in your knowledge/ understanding may be.

☐ **Practise against the clock:** Write a complete answer to the question along the lines of your planned outline. Do this against the clock, allowing yourself the time that would be allocated in the exam itself. Don't use any notes or textbook during this exercise.

☐ **I isolated major topics:** Be certain to isolate the major topics in your revision and learn them very well. While going over the contents of your notes, try to anticipate possible examination questions.

☐ **I rewrote the main points as I went through my notes:** Keep writing down the main points as you go through your notes. The writing process will fix the ideas in your mind.

☐ **I prepared for aurals and orals months in advance:** It's not good enough to start preparing for aural and oral sections of the exam paper a week or two before the test takes place. Practice at the start of the course and continue right through the year. Know the amount of marks awarded for these sections and be sure to give a fair proportion of study time to them.

☐ **Revising**
When you are first introduced to a topic in class you may understand it, but most of what you learn will be forgotten if you don't revise. In fact, research shows us that without revision we will lose up to 90% of what we learn within 6 months. Revision helps you retain the material for a longer period of time. Revising also helps increase your understanding of the topic.

☐ **Revisit the material covered in class within two days:** Educational psychologists have discovered that it is most important to revise within 24 hours of first learning something. This will often be in the form of homework.

☐ **I included some revision in each study session:** I set aside time at each study session to revise questions or topics I had learned in the past.

☐ **I became part of a study group:** Four students in my class set up a study group. We would each prepare a topic and teach it to the group. Each person would have a set amount of time to teach the topic. This worked well because we had definite starting and finishing times. We gave about an hour and a half each week to this kind of learning.

#7. Examination Performance

Tick any tips which you think might benefit you. Choose one of these which you can realistically improve on during the next term, and write it into your Study Behaviour Action Planner.

☐ **Read the questions and instructions!** Check the instructions at the beginning of each test paper carefully. There may be a small change in the exam format from year to year. Read each question carefully. Highlight or underline the key words and phrases.

☐ **Check for compulsory questions:** Tick the questions that must be answered in each section. Then tick off the question(s) you are likely to answer (using a different colour or symbol).

☐ **Allocate time for each question:** This should be done before the exam itself. The amount of time spent on each question will be determined by the percentage of the overall marks going for the question. For example, the time you allow will double if the marks awarded are double those of other questions. Allow at least five to ten minutes at the start of the test to read over the paper and ten minutes at the end to read your answers.

☐ **I began with my best question:** I began my exam with the question I felt I could best answer. By doing this, I built confidence in my ability to tackle the remainder of the test.

☐ **I plan my answers:** Jot down an outline of your answer by noting the main points before beginning to work on the full answer. It is useful to let the examiner see this work.

☐ **Avoid clutter:** Remember to allow plenty of space between points and sections and label all your answers clearly. Do everything you can to make the job of the examiner easier.

☐ **Keep an eye on the time:** If you run over the allotted time when dealing with a question it may be better to leave a space and continue to the next question. Above all, avoid the disaster of not having time to attempt all the required number of questions.

☐ **Don't waffle:** There are simply no marks going for repeating the same points or ideas. Be as clear and concise as you can. This does not mean that you don't explain things fully and give examples.

☐ **I recognise typical question formats:** Know exactly what is expected of you in an exam when asked to Compare, Contrast, Define, Discuss, Explain, Trace, Summarise, Describe or Outline. Take special note of words such as *"including"*, *"and"*, or *"or"*.

☐ **If you have time to spare, re-read your work:** Don't stop working on your paper before time is up. There are no extra marks awarded for being finished early. Your exam is designed to be undertaken within the time allocated. If you have time left after you read over your paper read over it a second time. Ideas may come to you even at this final stage.

☐ **Use notes:** It could happen that you discover that you have done something wrong, left a question out or perhaps misread a question. If time is not on your side, lay the correct answer out in note form first. Then elaborate on the notes. Try not to panic.

☐ **Bring a drink!** Bring a drink of water into the exam hall with you in order to avoid dehydration.

Exercise: Study Behaviour Action Planner

Write down your Action Plans to help you make the changes you need in order to get the exam results you want. Start with a few suggestions from the preceding pages, and add to the list over time. Revisit this page later to rate how much effort you've put into your plans. Add new plans as you need them. Don't write anything here that you don't intend to act and follow through on!

	Date Started	Date Reviewed	Self Rating
I will...			☆☆☆☆☆
I will...			☆☆☆☆☆
I will...			☆☆☆☆☆
I will...			☆☆☆☆☆
I will...			☆☆☆☆☆
I will...			☆☆☆☆☆
I will...			☆☆☆☆☆
I will...			☆☆☆☆☆
I will...			☆☆☆☆☆

Remember to reset your targets if you improve your
study performance - see page 121

www.careersportal.ie
Reach+

PRACTICAL

STEM

SCIENCE

Technology

Geography*

Construction Studies

Home Economics*

Agricultural Science

Biology*

Chemistry

Engineering

Physical Education

Biology*

Accounting

Physics

Applied Maths

Business

BUSINESS

Mathematics

Computer Science

Economics

Design & Comm Graphics

LCVP Link Modules

ARTISTIC & CREATIVE

Music

Home Economics*

Art

Gaeilge

Geography*

Politics & Society

English

Latin

SOCIAL

Modern Languages

Ancient Greek

History

Religious Education

Classical & Hebrew Studies

HUMANITIES

REALIST · NATURALIST · INVESTIGATIVE · ADMINISTRATIVE · CREATIVE · ENTERPRISING · LINGUISTIC · SOCIAL

**Leaving Cert Subjects,
Career Interests**
and the
World of Work

Some subjects have significant content spanning two areas

Subject Choice for Leaving Cert

Deciding what to study for the Leaving Cert puts you in charge of your own education. Although you will have to study English, Maths and Irish (unless exempt), you will have the choice to select another four or more subjects. You will also be able to choose at which level to study the subject, Higher or Ordinary level (or Foundation in the case of Maths and Irish).

Ideally, your non-compulsory subjects should be chosen simply because you are interested in them.

- If you plan to go directly into a job after school, then your choice of subjects doesn't usually matter.
- If you plan to do a PLC / FET (Further Education and Training) course after school then your choice of subjects doesn't usually matter, though it helps to have studied subjects that might be related to your choice of course (see 'Useful Subjects' below).
- If you intend to go directly to college for a CAO / HE (Higher Education) course (especially the Ordinary and Honours Degree courses, and less so the Certificate courses) then you may have to have certain Leaving Certificate subjects in order to be eligible.

Examples of Subject Requirements for CAO / HE courses

A number of degree programmes require **at least one** of the following subjects for entry: Chemistry, Physics, Accounting, Biology, Maths, Irish, French, German, Italian, English or Spanish. Some science courses require two science subjects, and many courses require a modern language, i.e. not Latin or Greek. A few courses also require specific grades, e.g. 'Journalism & New Media' in University of Limerick requires a H4 in English*.

General Guidelines

If you have no particular career direction at the moment, or aren't sure what you will do after you leave school, then it may be best to keep your options for the future open. It's a good idea to choose *one modern language* and *one science subject*, and do at least *three subjects at Higher level*. So how do you choose which subjects to take?

Choosing Subjects: If in doubt – Check it out!

You will probably have an idea about most subjects based on your experience of the Junior Cert. However, you may wish to know more before committing to a subject for the next two years. Use the **Subject Choice for LC Tool** in the **World of Education** tab of your online **Reach⁺** Career File to explore each subject you are interested in. Explore the following for each of the subjects you are considering:

- What does the course actually cover – and do the topics interest me?
  (Follow link to full Curriculum if necessary)

- What do the exam questions look like?
  (Check links to past exam papers and marking schemes)

- What is the format of the exam - is there continuous assessment, more than one paper, practicals? Which do I prefer?

- Do I have the aptitude / interest / talent for the subject?

- Is the subject an essential requirement for any third level courses I may be interested in?
  (Check the Third Level Entry Requirements)

- What do others who took the subject say about it?
  (Read the Videos & Interviews section on each subject)

* Always check for the latest published information as entry requirements can change from year to year.

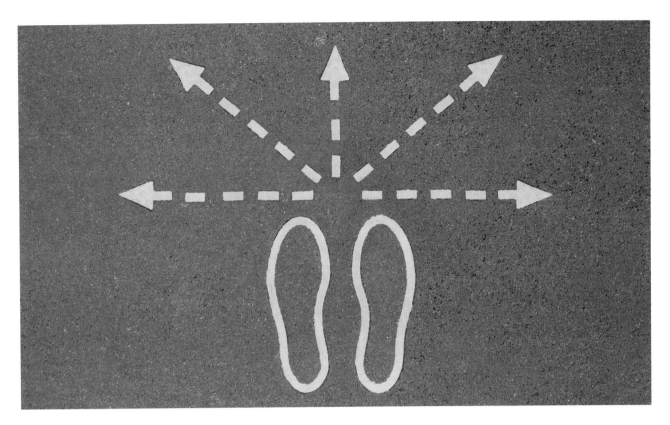

Choosing 'Useful' Subjects

Some Leaving Certificate subjects are seen as *useful* or helpful for college courses, e.g. business is useful for all business related courses. Choosing subjects that are related in some way to career areas you think you might like to work in is recommended. Not only do you get a better feel for the subject and confirm that you really do enjoy studying it, but you will also be more familiar with the language and terminology it uses when you go to college. To help you choose useful subjects, complete the exercise **Useful Subjects for Career Sectors** on the next page.

Choosing 'Essential' Subjects

Some colleges insist that you have particular subjects in order to be eligible to take certain courses, which makes the subject *essential* for the course. You will have to check the specific third level course to see what subjects are required to be eligible. Use the CourseFinder Tool in the **World of Education** tab of your **Reach⁺** Career File to find the course, and follow the links in the Entry Requirements section to check the entry requirements. Essential subjects are clearly related to the course – e.g. English for Journalism, Maths for Engineering, Chemistry for Pharmacy, etc.

If you are thinking of not doing a particular subject and want to see how this will affect your CAO choices, then check the Subject Choices for LC Tool for the subject you are thinking of, and check the '**3rd Level Requirements**' section. This will indicate what courses require this subject for entry or not.

Minimum Requirements

Your choice of subjects for the Leaving Certificate could prevent you from entering some colleges or courses. Read through and complete the checklist in the **Minimum Requirements** topic on page 136 before deciding on your subjects!

My School can't offer me the choices I want!

Sometimes your school can't offer you the subjects you want to study. In these cases you may have to compromise and select a subject you are less interested in. We recommend you always discuss this situation with your Guidance Counsellor.

Exercise: Useful Subjects for Career Sectors

The following exercise may help you decide what subjects to choose from those offered by your school. Although there are about 30 possible subject options available, most schools can only offer a limited number. Apart from the compulsory subjects (English, Maths and Irish) you need to choose four from those available. If you choose a modern language, your choice comes down to just three.

Using the Subject and Career Sectors Grid:

1. From the list of Leaving Certificate subjects across the top, cross off those that are not available in your school.
2. From the list of Career Sectors on the left, **underline** at least four sectors that interest you most. See page 176 for information on the sectors.
3. Prioritise your career sectors by entering a **score** (5 for your favourite sector, then 4, 3, 2 etc) in the rightmost column of the grid.
4. Write the score for each sector into each shaded box along the row for that sector.
5. For each subject column, add up the scores you've entered in the shaded boxes, and put this score in the bottom row (Subject Score) of the grid.
6. The highest scoring subjects are those likely to be the most useful for the options you are considering.

Example: Enda's Subject Choices

Enda's strongest interest is in the area of sport and fitness, followed by veterinary medicine and others. He gives his top score 5 for 'Leisure, Sport & Fitness', 4 for 'Animals & Veterinary' and so on down the list. He completed the grid as follows:

The scores from the grid (highest to lowest) suggest Biology, Business, Home Economics, Chemistry followed by a Modern Language (Note that Ag. Science and Physical Ed. are not available in his school).

Enda chose Biology and Home Economics, but for his third subject he choose History, as he has always enjoyed it. He disliked Business, so chose not to take it. Though History is not a 'useful' subject for his top career areas, he expects to do well with it and gain high points as a result, which he may need to get the college course he wants.

Career Sector	Engineering	Technology	Agricultural Science	Biology	Chemistry	Physics	Design & Comm Graphics	Computer Science	Art	Music	Modern Languages	History	Geography	Politics & Society	Home Economics	Economics	Business	LCVP Link Modules	Score
Animals & Veterinary			4	4	4														4
Farming, Horticulture & Forestry			2	2	2								2		2		2		2
Food & Beverages																			
Maritime, Fishing & Aquaculture																			
Construction, Property & Architecture																			
Physics, Mathematics & Space Science																			
Leisure, Sport & Fitness	5		5							5					5		5		5
Healthcare																			
Psychology & Social Care																			
Art, Craft & Design	1	1	1					1	1	1	1			1		1	1		1
Fashion & Beauty																			
Media, Film & Publishing																			
Music & Performing Arts		3	3						3	3	3					3	3		3
Community & Voluntary																			
Transport & Logistics																			
Subject Score	1	1	4	8	6	11	6		3	1	4	4	5	1		2		8	11

Subjects and Career Sectors Grid

Subject Groups	Practical					Science						Art				Humanities / Social					Business				
	Construction Studies	Engineering	Technology	Physical Education	Agricultural Science	Biology	Chemistry	Physics	Applied Maths	Computer Science	Design & Comm Graphics	Art	Music	Modern Languages	Classical Studies / Latin / Greek	History	Geography	Politics & Society	Religious Education	Home Economics	Economics	Accounting	Business	LCVP Link Modules	
Animals & Veterinary					■	■	■																		
Farming, Horticulture & Forestry					■	■	■										■				■		■		
Food & Beverages						■	■										■			■			■		
Maritime, Fishing & Aquaculture		■	■														■						■		
Architecture, Construction & Property	■		■					■			■	■					■								
Biological, Chemical & Pharmaceutical Science		■				■	■			■															
Biomedical Technologies & MedTech		■				■	■	■		■															
Computers & ICT		■						■	■	■															
Earth & Environment			■			■	■										■								
Engineering & Manufacturing	■	■	■				■	■	■		■														
Physics, Mathematics & Space Science		■	■				■	■	■												■				
Leisure, Sport & Fitness				■		■														■			■		
Healthcare				■		■	■													■					
Psychology & Social Care						■												■							
Art, Craft & Design	■		■								■	■								■					
Fashion & Beauty			■			■	■					■								■			■		
Media, Film & Publishing			■							■	■	■	■										■		
Music & Performing Arts												■	■										■		
Community & Voluntary						■											■	■	■	■					
Education & Teaching	■	■	■	■	■	■	■	■	■	■	■	■	■	■	■	■	■	■	■	■	■	■	■		
Government, Politics & EU																■	■	■			■				
Law & Legal																■		■							
Security, Defence & Law Enforcement				■													■								
History, Culture & Languages														■	■	■	■		■						
Accountancy & Taxation																					■	■	■		
Banking & Financial Services										■											■	■	■		
Insurance										■											■	■	■		
Advertising, Marketing & Public Relations										■		■									■		■		
Business Management & Human Resources																					■	■	■		
Clerical & Administration																					■	■	■		
Sales, Retail & Purchasing																					■	■	■		
Tourism & Hospitality														■			■	■			■		■		
Transport & Logistics		■	■														■				■	■	■		

Subject Score: [ ]

Signature

Minimum Requirements

Imagine getting your Leaving Certificate results with more than enough points for your chosen course, only to find that you are not offered a place! How could this happen?

It happens to a number of students every year, and it's usually because the student does not have the 'Minimum Entry Requirements' for the course and/or college. Getting a place in college is competitive, and there are a number of barriers to be overcome before you get accepted.

Barrier 1: Matriculation Requirements

To be allowed into a college for *any* course, you must meet the college *'matriculation requirements'*. Colleges each have their own rules, so you need to research the rules for the colleges you are interested in.

Examples...

 The specific details of what colleges accept (i.e. what subjects/grades) can change from year to year. Always check for the most up-to-date information available online, or with the colleges themselves.

The National University of Ireland (See Panel)

Requires six subjects: English, Irish and four others from the Leaving Certificate. Two of these subjects must be at least Grade H5 on the Higher Course, and at least Grade H7 or O6 in four other subjects.

A third language is sometimes required for some degree programmes – check each course individually to see if a 3rd language is required.

Foundation level maths accepted for purposes of entry requirement for some courses where Higher or Ordinary Level maths not a course requirement.

National University of Ireland (NUI) Colleges

- University College Dublin
- University College Cork
- National University of Ireland, Galway
- Maynooth University

NUI Member Institutes:

- Royal College of Surgeons in Ireland
- Shannon College of Hotel Management
- National College of Art and Design, Dublin
- Institute of Public Administration
- St. Angela's College, Sligo

Trinity College Dublin (TCD) / University of Limerick (UL) / Dublin City University

Requires six subjects, two (three for TCD and DCU's BEd) of which must be at least Grade H5 on the Higher Course.

Subjects must include a O6/H7 in English or Irish and Maths in **DCU**.

Subjects must include English and Maths and a language other than English (e.g., Irish/Latin/French etc) in **TCD**.

Mathematics at foundation-level is acceptable for minimum entry requirements only for some courses.

Technological Universities & Institutes of Technology (IOTs)

For Level 8 Honours degrees, 6 Leaving Certificate subjects, with at least Grade H5 in 2 subjects on the Higher Course and Grade O6/H7 in 4 other subjects, including Maths and either Irish or English.

For Levels 6 and 7 (Higher Certificate and Ordinary Degrees): 5 Leaving Certificate subjects at Grade O6/H7, including Maths and either Irish or English.

Foundation level maths accepted for purposes of entry requirement where Higher or Ordinary Level maths not a course requirement.

Examples, continued....

Colleges of Education (See Panel)

Colleges of education provide specialised training for primary school teachers. They require a minimum of 3 Grade H5s on the Higher Course and three O6/H7s. There are specific minimum grades for Irish (H4), Maths (O4/H7) and English (O4/H7).

Foundation Level Mathematics does not satisfy the entry requirement in Mathematics

Colleges of Education:
- DCU Institute of Education, Dublin 9
- Mary Immaculate College, Limerick
- Froebel Department of Primary and Early Childhood Education, Maynooth University
- Marino Institute of Education, Dublin 9

Barrier 2: Subject Requirements

Many courses build upon your learning in the Leaving Certificate. For this reason, these courses expect that you have achieved at least an ordinary level Grade O6, and sometimes a higher level Grade H5 in relevant subjects. For example, to study Veterinary Medicine in UCD you are expected to have a higher level H5 in chemistry. There are many such examples.

So even if you get enough points for a course you are looking at, you must also have the right subject combinations and grades to be accepted. The exact requirements for every course are presented each year in the college prospectus and online. You need to research each individual course you apply for to ensure you are eligible [see Exercise: Will that course suit me?, p21].

When researching, watch out for various subject requirements – what grades and levels are required, what subject combinations are accepted, and what alternative options may be available. For example, TCD will treat a higher level Grade H4 *or* an ordinary level Grade O2 in mathematics as acceptable for some courses.

Restricted Courses

Some CAO / HE courses are termed Restricted Courses. This is because they have early assessment procedures, such as interviews, portfolio assessment etc. Examples include many Art, Design and Music courses, which require a portfolio, and Medicine which requires an Aptitude test. Without these additional requirements you cannot apply for these courses. Many PLC / FET courses require an interview, and some require a portfolio or similar, so again you will need to do research to see if you meet the individual course requirements.

Note:
- You can view an up-to-date list of Restricted CAO / HE courses from the **CAO - HE Choices App** in the **World of Education** tab of your **REACH⁺** Career File

Exercise: Minimum Requirements [CAO / Higher Ed]

The following is a checklist that can be used to check if you are eligible for a CAO / HE course that you are considering. Select a course you would consider and fill in the following checklist.

Note: All this information can be accessed online or in the relevant college prospectus.

Course Code / Name: _____ / _____

Requirements		Tips	Criteria Met?
General Subject Requirements (minimum subjects and grades)		(e.g: 2 H5, 4 O6/H7)	
How many Higher grades required?		enter number	
Can results be taken from more than one sitting of the leaving cert for matriculation?	Y / N		
Can CAO Points be taken from more than one sitting?	Y / N		
Do you need Irish?	Y / N		
If at Higher Level, what grade?		enter only if specified	
If at Ordinary Level, what grade?		enter only if specified	
Is Foundation Level acceptable?	Y / N		
If exempted: I will be responsible for sending in an Exemption Application form and any additional paperwork directly to the college.		If you have an exemption, tick here to show you know the extra work needed to get your exemption accepted by the college	
Do you need English?	Y / N		
If at Higher Level, what grade?		enter only if specified	
If at Ordinary Level, what grade?		enter only if specified	
If you are taking a non-leaving cert English award, will it be accepted?	Y / N	check with college	
Do you need Maths?	Y / N		
If at Higher Level, what grade?		enter only if specified	
If at Ordinary Level, what grade?		enter only if specified	
Is Foundation Level acceptable?	Y / N		
Will a grade in Applied Maths be accepted as an alternative?	Y / N		
Does the college have a 'second chance' Maths exam if I don't get the required grade in my Leaving Cert?	Y / N		
Do you need a second language?	Y / N		
Is Irish accepted as a second language?	Y / N		
Is a specific language required?		enter the language if Yes	
What language will I present with?		enter the language you will use as your second language	
If at Higher Level, what grade?		enter only if specified	

If at Ordinary Level, what grade?		enter only if specified	
If exempt: I will be responsible for sending in a Exemption Application form and any additional paperwork directly to the college.		If you have an exemption, tick here to show you know the extra work needed to get your exemption accepted by the college	
Do you need a third Language?	Y / N		
What specific languages are required that I may have.		If yes to above, check that your third language meets the course requirements	
If at Higher Level, what grade?		enter only if specified	
If at Ordinary Level, what grade?		enter only if specified	
Do you need a Laboratory Science Subject?	Y / N		
What Lab Science subject will I have that is acceptable?		Note that some courses specify specific leaving cert science courses only. Some require two Lab Science subjects.	
If at Higher Level, what grade?		enter only if specified	
If at Ordinary Level, what grade?		enter only if specified	
Will I be presenting with science subjects which cannot both be used together?	Y / N	e.g. 'Physics' and 'Physics & Chemistry' may not be used together for matriculation.	
Other Subjects - any specific requirement?		enter only if specified	
Will I be presenting with any combinations of subjects not accepted together?		e.g. 'Physics & Chemistry' may not be presented with 'Physics'. If subjects have significant overlap they may not be both allowed.	
Other Considerations:			
CAO Points range:		Note last years points and if the trend is increasing or decreasing	
Compensation rule available?		e.g. H7 accepted in required subject if 3 H5 or 1 H3+1H5 in other papers.	
Portfolio required?	Y / N		
HPAT / Entrance test required?	Y / N		
Suitability test required?	Y / N	e.g. some courses in TUD	
Interview required?	Y / N		
Further education places available? (Higher Education Links Scheme)	Y / N		
Leaving Cert Applied (LCA) accepted?	Y / N		
Leaving Cert Vocational (LCVP) accepted?	Y / N		
Disability route available (DARE)?	Y / N		
Non Irish awards accepted?		e.g. A-Levels, IB programme	
Other			

Qualifications and Levels

Whatever you want to do in life, there is a qualification which can help. What's important is to choose the right ones at the right times in your life. To do this, you need to know how they fit together.

Most qualifications available in Ireland fit into the National Framework of Qualifications (NFQ), which divides qualifications into **ten levels**. Entry at Level 1 is at the bottom and Level 10 is at the top. Levels can include different types of qualifications, for example Certificates, Degrees, and Diplomas. Some are awarded for a broad general education (e.g. the Junior and Leaving Certificates), while others are vocational: they prepare for a particular employment sector, such as a FET Certificate in Childcare. Others combine both.

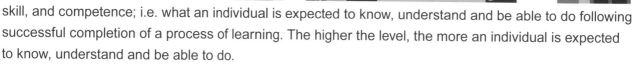

The levels are based on nationally agreed standards of knowledge, skill, and competence; i.e. what an individual is expected to know, understand and be able to do following successful completion of a process of learning. The higher the level, the more an individual is expected to know, understand and be able to do.

The system of levels is arranged like a ladder. Completion of one level usually means you are able to move up to the next, or jump several if you commit to an agreed number of years study. For example, it is possible for you to progress from a good honours Leaving Cert (Level 5) directly to an Honours Bachelors Degree (Level 8) if you commit to the three or four years (sometimes more) of study required. This is the normal route for students going to University.

Alternatively, from the Leaving Cert you can choose to move one step at a time by selecting a Level 6 Higher Certificate in an Institute of Technology / Technology University, then a Level 7 Ordinary Degree, and eventually a Level 8 Honours Degree in the same or a different institution.

The National Framework of Qualifications makes it relatively easy to move through the education system, and is internationally recognised (meaning that universities and employers in other countries will understand your qualification), which is important if you choose to study or work abroad. An interactive version of the fan diagram above can be found online at www.qqi.ie which explains all of the levels and awards available. It is summarised in the ladder diagram on the following page:

Progression Routes:
The National Framework helps to improve **access** (entry) to education and training. It allows you transfer and progress within and between courses and colleges nationally and internationally.

An Award – Who Says So?
It's very important that a country controls who gives out awards and for what. If there was no control on who gave awards how would we know what standard had been achieved?

An **awarding body** is a national body that has the legal power to grant an award which recognises learning. Examples include the State Examination Commission, QQI, Universities, and Institutes of Technology.

The NFQ summarised

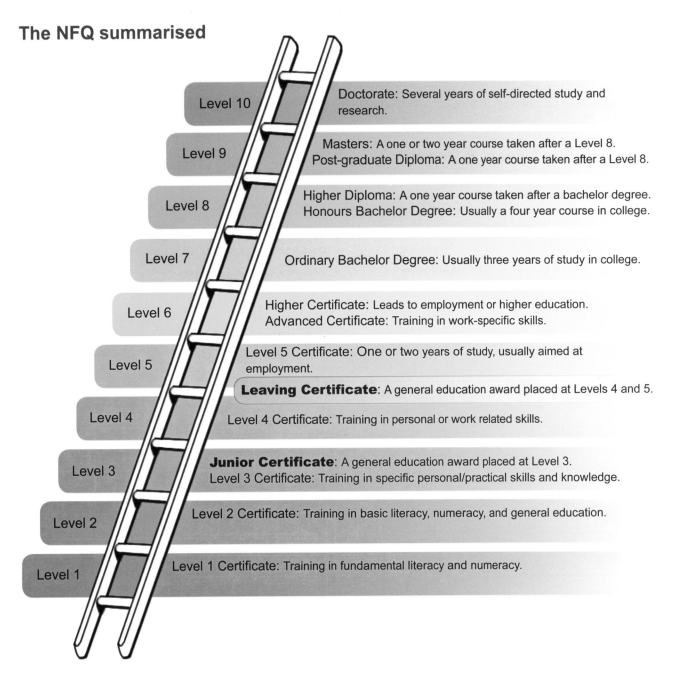

Level 10 — Doctorate: Several years of self-directed study and research.

Level 9 — Masters: A one or two year course taken after a Level 8.
Post-graduate Diploma: A one year course taken after a Level 8.

Level 8 — Higher Diploma: A one year course taken after a bachelor degree.
Honours Bachelor Degree: Usually a four year course in college.

Level 7 — Ordinary Bachelor Degree: Usually three years of study in college.

Level 6 — Higher Certificate: Leads to employment or higher education.
Advanced Certificate: Training in work-specific skills.

Level 5 — Level 5 Certificate: One or two years of study, usually aimed at employment.
Leaving Certificate: A general education award placed at Levels 4 and 5.

Level 4 — Level 4 Certificate: Training in personal or work related skills.

Level 3 — **Junior Certificate**: A general education award placed at Level 3.
Level 3 Certificate: Training in specific personal/practical skills and knowledge.

Level 2 — Level 2 Certificate: Training in basic literacy, numeracy, and general education.

Level 1 — Level 1 Certificate: Training in fundamental literacy and numeracy.

Six good reasons why you should take qualifications seriously

#1. To give yourself a **choice of jobs**: increasingly many low-skilled jobs are being exported to foreign countries, or being automated by machines. As a result, there are few low-skilled jobs left to choose from.

#2. To **get promoted**: it is difficult to move from unskilled labour to skilled labour without actually acquiring any skills. Qualifications are designed to give you the skills you need to move up.

#3. To make **money**: on average, there is a huge pay gap between people with qualifications and people without. The highest paid jobs are usually those which take a lot of skill, and qualifications are there to teach those skills.

#4. To **prove your competence**: qualifications are proof that you are capable of mastering a body of knowledge, and have the skills which employers value. Not only does a qualification show that you are good at what you do; it suggests that you are able to become even better!

#5. To show **commitment**: your investment of time and effort in a qualification shows employers that you are serious about what you want to do, and that any further investments they make in your training will not go to waste.

#6. To **enjoy yourself**: learning about something which you enjoy is fulfilling, boosts your self-confidence, and improves self-awareness.

Exercise: Qualifications and Jobs

Take a look at the list of jobs below, and fill in what you think would be the typical level of education needed to get the job, and what range of wages the job usually earns. Do you notice any pattern in the answers? Your Guidance Counsellor will give you the correct answers when you're done. How many did you get right?

Qualification Levels & Zones:

ZONE	EXPERIENCE	EDUCATION
1	"On the job" training:	The job requires a low level of training given as part of the job
2	Level 5 Certificate:	The job requires a Leaving Cert or QQI Level 5 Certificate
3	Level 6 Certificate:	The job requires at least a QQI Level 6 Certificate
4	Level 7/8 Bachelors Degree:	The job requires at least a Level 7 or 8 Bachelors Degree
5	Level 9/10 Postgraduate Award:	The job requires more than an Honours Bachelors Degree

Job Title	ZONE					Salary Range					Correct?
	1	2	3	4	5	20k	40k	60k	80k	100k+	
(Example) Fashion Model:	■					■					✓
Forklift Operator:											
Sales Assistant, Retail:											
Bus Driver:											
Legal Secretary:											
Childcare Worker:											
Hairdresser:											
Plumber:											
Mechanic:											
Advertising / PR Manager:											
School Teacher - Primary School:											
Nurse - General:											
Engineer - Mechanical:											
Engineer – Software:											
Human Resources Manager:											
Pharmacist:											
Doctor (GP):											
Lecturer - 3rd Level:											
Bono (U2):											
Entrepreneur:											

Note:

- Use the **Career Explorer App** in your **Reach⁺** Career File to research education levels and typical earnings for all occupations.

Money Matters

Going to College – What will it cost?

For many students and families, going to college puts a big strain on their financial situation. Knowing what it will cost, and planning to cover costs in advance will help remove some of this stress. When looking at the cost of going to college, it is useful to break down the costs into the following categories:

- **One-off costs:** Usually at the beginning of the year.
- **Monthly expenses:** Items which are normally billed monthly or average out over a monthly period.
- **Weekly expenses:** The day to day living costs. (Note: some months have 5 weeks!)

There are two big decisions that effect the costs of going to college – *where* and *how long*. Studying locally for a one or two year course may cost much the same as going to school. On the other hand, studying away from home (in Ireland or abroad) for three or more years can cost a lot of money. For many students, the choice of college will be a financial decision. Knowing this can effect your choice of courses, so it is important to explore the real costs of going to college, and to see if there are any grants and supports available to help you with your decision.

> **Note:**
> - As costs are changing all the time, you can get current examples and estimates in the **Money Matters App** in the **World of Education** tab of your **Reach⁺** Career File.

College life usually lasts up to 8 months per year, and there are approximately 35 weeks during this time.

Complete the exercise on the next page to help you estimate the cost for *one year* of attending a course, living either **at home**, or **away from home**.

Useful Websites...

www.studentfinance.ie	– Financial supports for Further and Higher Education
www.susi.ie	– Student Grants
www.mabs.ie	– Money Advice & Budgeting
www.nca.ie	– National Consumer Agency
www.google.ie	– For everything else!

Exercise – Calculating College Costs

Living Away from Home

One off Costs:	Estimated:
College registration fees	
Books?	
IT equipment?	
Stationary?	
Course equipment / materials?	
Student travel card?	
Car/Motorbike costs (purchase, taxes, insurance, servicing etc)	
First oil stock-up?	
First food stock-up	
Search for accommodation	
Deposit & rent in advance	
Other?	
Total One-off Costs:	

Monthly Costs:	Estimated:
Medical / medication	
Clothes	
Mobile / data credit	
Personal expenses (makeup / hygiene)	
Contribution to household	
Books / photocopying credit	
Loans (if any)	
Bin charges	
Broadband / internet	
Fuel / heating	
Electricity	
Other?	
Total Monthly Costs:	

Weekly Costs:	Estimated:
Travel to/from college	
Weekend travel / transport	
College food / snacks	
Entertainment / socialising	
Petrol/Diesel costs	
Groceries / food / utilities	
Other?	
Total Weekly Costs:	

One off Costs:		×1 =	
Monthly Costs:		×8 =	
Weekly Costs:		×35 =	
		Yearly Total:	

Living At Home

One off Costs:	Estimated:
College registration fees:	
Books?	
IT equipment?	
Stationary?	
Course equipment / materials?	
Student travel card?	
Car/Motorbike costs (purchase, taxes, insurance, servicing etc)	
Other…	
Total One-off Costs:	

Monthly Costs:	Estimated:
Medical / medication	
Clothes	
Mobile / data credit	
Personal expenses (makeup / hygiene)	
Contribution to household	
Books / photocopying credit	
Loans (if any)	
Total Monthly Costs:	

Weekly Costs:	Estimated:
Travel to/from college	
Weekend travel / transport	
College food / snacks	
Entertainment / socialising	
Petrol/Diesel costs	
Other?	
Total Weekly Costs:	

One off Costs:		×1 =	
Monthly Costs:		×8 =	
Weekly Costs:		×35 =	
		Yearly Total:	

Reach+

Income

To cover these costs, you will need to ensure you have sufficient money. Students finance themselves in various ways, some families will cover the entire cost, others will use a combination of grants, bank loans, part time work, and savings to meet the costs.

In the table below, fill in the estimated amounts of money that you may have available to cover your costs.

Income:	Estimated:
Savings	
Earnings from work over the summer	
Earnings from part-time work during college	
Grants / allowances	
Scholarships	
Parents	
Other?	
Total Income:	

Will you have enough?

For your first year in college, calculate whether you are likely to have sufficient money to cover the costs:

Income:	
Total Yearly Costs (calculated page opposite):	-
Available funds:	=

If the number in the yellow box above is negative (your costs are greater than your income), you will have a deficit, and will either have to spend less, or find additional sources of funding. Are any of the options on the right available to you?

Note: taking out a loan will add repayments to your monthly costs!

Options for meeting a deficit:

Bank Loan

Credit Union Loan

Student Grant

Fund for Students with Disabilities

Student Assistance Fund

Back to Education Allowance

Maintenance Grant

Free Course Fees

Subject based Scholarships

Area Based Grants

Scholarships

Tips:
- Use the **Money Matters App** in the **World of Education** tab of your **Reach⁺** Career File to automatically calculate your costs.
- Use the **Scholarships Tool** in the **World of Education** tab of your **Reach⁺** Career File to explore possible scholarships you migh be eligible for.

CAO - Choices

The CAO application system encourages each student to select courses in order of preference from two separate lists:

- Levels 6 / 7 Higher Certificates and Ordinary Degrees, and

- Level 8 Honours Degrees.

There are courses in many disciplines that you can study at third level. The chart shows recent data on the number of students who chose courses from six broad study areas. The data shows CAO first preference choices - and provides clues to what students across Ireland would like to study.

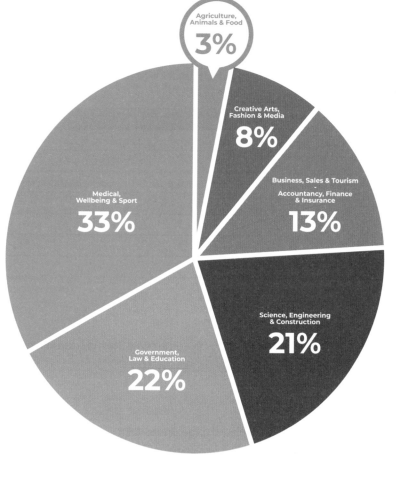

#1. Are you surprised with the distribution? Do you think your class would show a similar distribution?

#2. Which broad study area(s) might you choose?

#3. Discuss the distribution with your class and have your Guidance Counsellor give his/her view.

Because selecting a course of study after the Leaving Cert is such an important decision, we will take you through a number of exercises that will ensure that your decisions are well researched and well thought out.

Exercise #1. You will explore the many areas of study on offer and go on to select your preferences.

Exercise #2. You will consider the many factors involved in choosing a course and then decide what are the factors most important to you.

Exercise #3. You will go online to create a shortlist of courses that interest you most, and write your chosen courses into the grids on pages 153-154 for evaluation.

Exercise #4. You will place courses in order of preference ready for entering into the CAO application form.

Exercise: #1. Preparation

What area of study interests me most:

We will ask you to complete 5 steps that will help you choose courses that interest you most. This information will then be used in Exercise #3 to create a list of courses currently on offer through the CAO.

 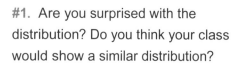

1 Career Sectors

On the following pages we ask you to look through a range of options that will enable you to create a list of sectors that suit you. Read down through the study areas below. Then starting at the top:

a) In the **first column** (A) place a ✓ if the area of study holds enough interest for you to warrant further consideration. Place an ✗ if you are sure you have no interest.

b) In the second column (B), number the items you have ticked, giving a 1 to the area that holds the greatest interest, 2 the second greatest and so on.

c) At the end of the exercise, fill in your top 3 preferences in the spaces provided.

	A	B

AGRICULTURE, ANIMALS & FOOD

Animals & Veterinary Science
This study area includes subjects such as veterinary science, animal physiology, animal nutrition, animal behaviour, equine business and wildlife.

Farming, Horticulture & Forestry
This study area includes subjects such as agricultural science, animal and crop production, farm management, forestry, horticulture and agribusiness.

Food & Beverages
This study area includes subjects such as food production, food innovation, food science, nutrition, food preparation, bar studies and bar management.

Maritime, Fishing & Aquaculture
This study area includes subjects such as oceanography, marine biology, environmental management, navigation and ship handling, conservation, seafood processing, and management skills for the fishing industry.

STEM, ENVIRONMENT & CONSTRUCTION

Biological, Chemical & Pharmaceutical Science
This study area includes subjects such as biological science, pharmaceutical science, chemistry and biochemistry. You may also study subjects such as cell biology, microbiology and molecular biology. Laboratory work often forms a substantial part of these courses.

Biomedical Technologies & MedTech
This study area includes subjects such as biotechnology, biomedical science, manufacturing engineering, and process engineering.

Computers & ICT
This broad study area includes subjects dealing with computer hardware (e.g. PCs, networking), software (e.g. operating systems, programming languages), computer science (e.g. theory, maths) to complete systems (e.g. process control systems, software / web applications).

Construction, Architecture & Property
This study area includes architecture, land and building surveying, construction management, building technology, interior design, quantity surveying, CAD, property management and estate agency.

Earth & Environment
This study area includes subjects such as environmental science, environmental management, conservation, geography, bioscience, earth science, oceanography, meteorology and energy engineering.

	A	B

Engineering, Manufacturing & Energy
This study area includes a wide variety of engineering subjects, such as electrical, mechanical, civil/structural (roads/bridges etc.), electronic, marine, aerospace, biomedical, energy and automation.

Physics, Mathematics & Space Science
This study area includes subjects such as physics, mathematics, statistics, computing, experimental physics, astronomy, optics, astrophysics, climate science, and earth science.

HEALTHCARE, WELLBEING & SPORT

Healthcare
This study area includes medicine, nursing, physiotherapy, dentistry, surgical training, nutrition, radiography, and pharmacy.

Leisure, Sport & Fitness
This study area includes subjects such as sports & exercise science, recreation management, technology & sports, sports coaching, aquatics, sports & leisure administration, equine business and physiology.

Psychology & Social Care
This study area includes subjects such as psychology, social studies, counselling, childhood studies, community/youth studies, sociology, and occupational therapy.

CREATIVE ARTS, FASHION & MEDIA

Art, Craft & Design
This study area includes subjects such as drawing, animation, painting, printmaking, ceramics, craft design, photography, art appreciation, visual & graphic design and product design.

Fashion & Beauty
This study area includes subjects such as fashion design, textile design, and related managerial positions.

Media, Film & Publishing
Study the techniques and theories of traditional media (newspaper, TV) and/or new digital media (Social Media, Internet), writing and editing, and research.

Music & Performing Arts
This study area includes subjects such as music, drama, film production, theatre, sound engineering or some other aspect of the entertainment industry.

GOVERNMENT, LAW & EDUCATION

Community & Voluntary
This study area includes such subjects such as community leadership, youth development, social studies, social research, social policy and community education.

Education & Teaching
Includes subjects that will lead to a qualification to teach or carry out other work in a school, college or other educational setting.

Government, Politics & EU
Study one or more of the following sample subjects: politics, economics, public policy, public administration, european law, human rights, capitalism, human welfare and company law.

Reach+

	A	B
History, Culture & Languages This broad study area includes subjects such as anthropology, languages, history, international culture, geography, archaeology, philosophy and classical studies.	☐	___
Law & Legal Includes legal research/writing, property law, human rights, politics, economics, public policy, labour law, or constitutional law.	☐	___
Security, Defence & Law Enforcement Includes subjects such as forensic investigation, computer security, criminal justice and police studies.	☐	___

ACCOUNTANCY, FINANCE & INSURANCE

	A	B
Accountancy & Taxation Study one or more of the following sample subjects: accountancy, economics, financial management, risk management, law, taxation.	☐	___
Banking & Financial Services Includes the following sample subjects: financial management, risk management, economics, banking, fund management and international finance.	☐	___
Insurance Includes courses that include subjects such as risk management, statistics, retail sales and actuarial studies.	☐	___

BUSINESS, SALES & TOURISM

	A	B
Advertising, Marketing & Public Relations This broad study area includes a range of business subjects with a special focus on topics such as market research, new business/product development, advertising and promotion, digital marketing and Public Relations (PR).	☐	___
Business Management & Human Resources This study area includes subjects that prepare you for a wide range of business roles such as business administration, management, human resources, marketing, business computing systems and business law.	☐	___
Clerical & Administration Includes subjects such as business studies, computer applications, office administration and management, and computerised accounts.	☐	___
Sales, Retail & Purchasing Study a range of subjects focused on sales, customer service, retail finance, retail law, purchasing, consumer behaviour, enterprise skills and retail management.	☐	___
Tourism & Hospitality Includes subjects such as tourism studies, hotel management, catering management, event management, tourism operations, bar supervision and often a foreign language.	☐	___
Transport & Logistics Includes subjects relating to the transportation of goods and people, such as warehousing skills, logistics, cabin crew training, airline studies, and fleet management.	☐	___

Area most interested in...	Second most interested area...	Third most interested area...
1 _____	2 _____	3 _____

2 Career Interests:
Select your Career Interests here to show courses that match your interests. You can select as many as you like. See pages 67 - 74 for more information on career interests:

Realist: ☐   Enterprising: ☐   Social: ☐   Linguistic: ☐

Administrative: ☐   Investigative: ☐   Creative: ☐   Naturalist: ☐

3 Regions:
What part of the country would you consider studying in? Studying away from home has significant cost implications. However, being prepared to study beyond your location may open up many more study opportunities. It costs nothing to look!

☐ **Dublin** *(Greater area)*   ☐ **Connacht**   ☐ **Leinster** *(excl. Dublin)*   ☐ **Munster**   ☐ **Ulster**

4 Colleges:
In which colleges would you like to study?

[   ]

Avoid confining your course search to one college unless you have a very good reason, as this restricts your choices!

5 Entry Requirements:
Many courses require you to have taken certain Leaving Cert subjects **and** achieve a number of CAO points to be eligable for entry. Your results will be converted into CAO points using a common scale *(see points calculator on back page)* using your top six grades. Your previous examination results should guide you as to the kind of CAO Points you might expect to achieve, but **do** allow for an improvement. You will gain more experience as you approach the Leaving Cert.

Enter your expected CAO points score here: [   ]
(add at least 50 to allow for improvement and yearly fluctuations)

Some courses have specific subject entry requirements. Tick the boxes that apply to you:

Maths Level:	Foundation ☐	Ordinary ☐	Higher ☐
Lab Science:	Yes ☐	No ☐	
Modern Language:	Yes ☐	No ☐	

Before using this information to create a list of courses, we need to know what we are looking for that makes a course worth applying to. Next we will decide on what we are looking for in a course.

Exercise: #2. Consider All Factors
This exercise will help you to choose courses that really interest and suit you. Each course and college you consider offers different opportunities. Read through the items on the following page and decide which factors are most important to you. Then add any of your own to the list. We then use this information when researching courses to see if the course meets your requirements.

a) In the first column (**A**) place a ✓ in the box if the item is important to you, or place an ✗ if it is not important.

b) Add your own factors at the end and mark them in the same way.

c) In the second column (**B**), number the items you have ticked, giving a 1 to the factor that is most important, 2 the second most important and so on. This should help you to establish what your priorities are.

d) Fill in the **Priority Grids** overleaf with the factors you just chose across the top. These grids are helpful tools which let you compare courses based on what's important to you. With your priorities written in, you will be ready to start adding some of the courses you are most interested (see Exercise #3, page 154).

Course Content:

The material on this course will keep me interested for several years. Give this a Star Rating based on how well the subject matches your interests.

	A	B

Career Focused:
I am pursuing a certain career or industry sector, and a course which leads me directly there is what I'm looking for.

Broad Subject Areas:
I am not sure what to focus on yet, so I want a course offering a broad introduction to an area and that will allow me to specialise when I understand more.

College Facilities:
The course I'm studying should have excellent academic facilities to improve my learning experience.

Hobbies and Interests:
I want a course in a college which allows me pursue my interests in sports or the arts.

Small Class Size:
I would like a course which accepts a relatively small number of students, where people get to know each other well.

Freedom:
I would like the opportunity to live away from home and manage my own life.

Work Experience:
Getting industrial experience as a part of my degree is important to me.

Study Abroad:
I wish to spend some time studying in a foreign university as a part of my degree.

Affordable:
I can handle the course fees, transport, accommodation, living costs, and expenditure on course materials comfortably.

Student Finances:
I want a course where I will be eligible for some form of financial support.

Scholarship:
I have a good chance of securing a scholarship if I attend this course.

Continuous Assessment:
I want a course with lots of continuous assessment to take the pressure off my final exams.

Reputation:
I want to graduate with a degree which is recognised and highly desirable in industry.

Electives:
The opportunity to study some subjects in which I am interested alongside my primary degree would be valuable to me.

Social Life:
I would like to study in a college with a reputation for an active social life and societies which suit my interests.

Other Factor:_____

Description:_____

Other Factor:_____

Description:_____

Exercise: #3. Research

In the previous exercises you identified how to search for courses and what to look for when you find them. In this exercise you go online and use the search criteria you choose in Exercise #1 to generate a list of courses. You then start to evaluate them according to your requirements set out in Exercise #2. You can do this using the **CAO - HE Choices App** online, or you can complete it here using college prospectuses and the **Priority Grids** provided on the next pages.

Online Version

Login to your **Reach+** Career File, select the **World of Education** tab and select the **CAO & HE Choices App.** Follow the Steps shown in the App as follows:

1. **Deciding Whats' Important**: Enter your choices from Exercise #2
2. **Find & Tag**: Use our CourseFinder tool and enter your selections from Exercise #1. If you like a course, 'tag' it [⭐]. Use other filters on the CourseFinder if required.
3. **Research & Evaluate**: The Level 8 courses you tagged will now be listed ready to be researched in detail, with links to all the information you need provided. For each course, select the Evaluate option and record your findings.
4. **Rank & Save**: Review your choices and arrange the list by dragging your top preferences to the top.
5. **Repeat** the last 2 steps for Level 7/6 courses.

Book Version

a) Fill in the top of the **Priority Grids** with the selections you made in Exercise #2
b) Using prospectuses from the colleges you are interested in, find courses relating to the Career Sectors you selected in Exercise #1
c) Enter the course code, college, title and points into the Level 8 and Level 6-7 Grids on the next pages.
d) Rate the course content from 1 - 5 by shading the stars, based on the information you read about the course.
e) Place a tick in the Grid where the college/course satisfies the 'Factors' that matter to you.
f) Repeat steps **c - e** for as many courses that interest you.

Example of completed Priority Grid:

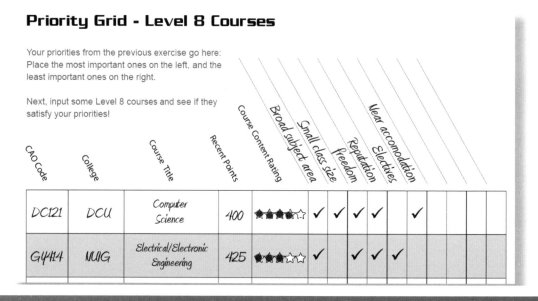

Priority Grid - Level 8 Courses

Your priorities from Exercise #2 go here: Place the most important ones on the left, and the least important ones on the right.

Next, input some Level 8 courses and see if they satisfy your priorities! See an example overleaf.

CAO Code	College	Course Title	Recent Points	Course Content Rating									
				☆☆☆☆☆									
				☆☆☆☆☆									
				☆☆☆☆☆									
				☆☆☆☆☆									
				☆☆☆☆☆									
				☆☆☆☆☆									
				☆☆☆☆☆									
				☆☆☆☆☆									
				☆☆☆☆☆									
				☆☆☆☆☆									
				☆☆☆☆☆									
				☆☆☆☆☆									
				☆☆☆☆☆									
				☆☆☆☆☆									

Priority Grid - Level 6-7 Courses

Your priorities from Exercise #2 go here: Place the most important ones on the left, and the least important ones on the right.

Next, input some Level 6/7 courses and see if they satisfy your priorities! See an example overleaf.

CAO Code	College	Course Title	Recent Points	Course Content Rating										
				☆☆☆☆☆										
				☆☆☆☆☆										
				☆☆☆☆☆										
				☆☆☆☆☆										
				☆☆☆☆☆										
				☆☆☆☆☆										
				☆☆☆☆☆										
				☆☆☆☆☆										
				☆☆☆☆☆										
				☆☆☆☆☆										
				☆☆☆☆☆										
				☆☆☆☆☆										
				☆☆☆☆☆										
				☆☆☆☆☆										

www.careersportal.ie

Reach+

Exercise: #4. Results

+ add to **Career Portfolio**

Review the information in each of your Priority Grids (or the equivalent ranked list online, CAO Choices, Step 7). The information you gathered should help guide you to make a decision on which courses to include on your CAO form, and in which order. Generally, the more stars you fill and ticks you have given on the left side of the grid, the closer the course matches your preferences. However, as you go through this exercise you may discover that you need more information, or that other items need to be considered. These can be added to your Grids and researched further.

Spend some time evaluating the courses until you are ready to decide on the order they should be put in your CAO application. Review and refine your lists as often as necessary. Next, list your courses **in order of preference**. This means:

⟶ Place the course which you **WANT** the most **FIRST**.
⟶ Make sure you are **ELIGIBLE** for every course on your list - check the Minimum Requirements p138.
⟶ Do **NOT** automatically exclude courses based on your expected points.

CAO Level 8 Courses			
Pref.	Code	Title	College
1			
2			
3			
4			
5			
6			
7			
8			
9			
10			

CAO Level 6/7 Courses			
Pref.	Code	Title	College
1			
2			
3			
4			
5			
6			
7			
8			
9			
10			

Signature

PLC Choices

Post Leaving Certificate (PLC) courses take place in schools, colleges and community education centres around the country. The courses are full-time and last for one to two years. They offer a mixture of "hands-on" practical work, academic study, and work experience. They are designed as a step towards skilled employment or further education. Students completing a PLC course are usually awarded a QQI Level 5 Certificate or QQI Level 6 Advanced Certificate (see the section on Qualifications in this workbook) or equivalent.

Exercise - PLC Courses

How much do you know about studying PLC courses? Answer the following questions by circling **T** for true, **?** if you don't know, or **F** for false for each question. Discuss your answers in class.

1	Post Leaving Cert courses are only for students who don't fill out a CAO form.	T ? F
2	I can only apply for one PLC course in each college.	T ? F
3	PLC courses usually focus on key skills needed for work.	T ? F
4	The qualification you get with PLC courses is not recognised internationally.	T ? F
5	If you do a PLC, you are almost guaranteed a place in a similar third level course in a University or Institute of Technology.	T ? F
6	The points needed for entry to PLC courses are lower than the points needed for entry to CAO.	T ? F
7	The tuition fees for PLC courses are government funded.	T ? F
8	Most applications to PLC courses involve sitting an interview.	T ? F
9	Far more students do CAO courses than PLC courses.	T ? F
10	Most students who apply to PLC courses get a place.	T ? F
11	I can make all my applications to PLC courses on one form, just like the CAO.	T ? F
12	Some third level college places are reserved for students who have earned qualifications from PLC courses.	T ? F
13	If I don't take a PLC course right after my Leaving Cert, I can't take one at all.	T ? F
14	I cannot apply for both PLC and CAO courses.	T ? F

Exercise: #1. Preparation

Selecting Courses:

On the following pages we ask you to look through a range of options that will enable you to create a list of courses that suit you. Read down through the study areas below. Then starting at the top:

a) In the **first column** (A) place a ✓ if the area of study holds enough interest for you to warrant further consideration. Place an ✗ if you are sure you have no interest.

b) In the second column (B), number the items you have ticked, giving a 1 to the area that holds the greatest interest, 2 the second greatest and so on.

c) At the bottom of the opposite page, fill in your top 3 preferences in the spaces provided.

	A	**B**

AGRICULTURE, ANIMALS & FOOD

Animals & Veterinary Science
This study area includes subjects such as animal care, animal health and welfare, animal science, equine studies and veterinary care.

Farming, Horticulture & Forestry
This study area includes subjects such as dairy and farm management, the environment, forestry, agribusiness or any other subject related to agriculture in Ireland and abroad.

Food & Beverages
This study area includes subjects such as food production, culinary arts, food science, nutrition, food preparation, bar studies and bar management.

Maritime, Fishing & Aquaculture
This study area includes subjects such as seafood processing, aquaculture, commercial fishing and skipper courses.

STEM, ENVIRONMENT & CONSTRUCTION

Biological, Chemical & Pharmaceutical Science
This study area includes subjects such as applied biology, laboratory science, pre-university science and pharmacy assistant.

Biomedical Technologies & MedTech
This study area includes subjects such as applied science techniques, health & safety, microbiology, laboratory techniques and medical laboratory science.

Computers & ICT
This broad study area includes subjects dealing with computer hardware (e.g. PCs, networking), software (e.g. operating systems, programming languages), computer science (e.g. theory, maths) to complete systems (e.g. process control systems, software / web applications).

Construction, Architecture & Property
Includes subjects such as preliminary engineering, construction technology, interior design, architectural and sustainable technology.

Earth & Environment
This study area includes subjects such as environmental science, environmental management, ecology, green energy and conservation.

Engineering, Manufacturing & Energy
This study area includes a wide variety of engineering and technology subjects, such as electrical, mechanical, motor vehicle technology, civil/structural (roads/bridges etc) and electronics.

A	B
☐	___

Physics, Mathematics & Space Science
This study area mostly requires Higher Education awards. Please refer to CAO / HE awards for courses leading into this sector.

A	B
☐	___

HEALTHCARE, WELLBEING & SPORT

Healthcare
Includes nursing studies, healthcare assistant, physiology, sports injury, dental nursing, pharmacy assistant, holistic therapies and related administrative roles.

Leisure, Sport & Fitness
Includes sports physiology, leisure management, outdoor recreation, sports development, coaching, sports and leisure business and administration.

Psychology & Social Care
Includes applied social studies, social and community care practice, disability care, special needs care and community/youth studies.

CREATIVE ARTS, FASHION & MEDIA

Art, Craft & Design
This study area includes subjects such as drawing, painting, printmaking, ceramics, craft design, photography, art appreciation, web design, graphic design, product design and fashion design.

Fashion & Beauty
Studying subjects such as fashion, craft and textile design, beauty care, hairdressing, and retail or administrative aspects of the business.

Media, Film & Publishing
Includes the areas of traditional and modern digital media: television, journalism, digital and social media.

Music & Performing Arts
This study area includes subjects such as music, drama, film production, theatre, animation, dance, games development and sound engineering.

GOVERNMENT, LAW & EDUCATION

Community & Voluntary
This area of study includes community development, social and community care, youth work, and health service skills.

Education & Teaching
Includes subjects that will lead to a qualification to work in areas such as: early years education and care settings, classroom or special needs assistant, and Montessori teaching.

Government, Politics & EU
This study area mostly requires Higher Education awards. Please refer to CAO / HE awards for courses leading into this sector.

www.careersportal.ie

Reach+

	A	B

History, Culture & Languages
This broad study area includes subjects such as cultural & heritige studies, 'English as foreign language' (EFL), European studies, liberal arts, culture and history.

Law & Legal
Includes legal studies, pre-university law, Legal secretarial/administration studies, and business law.

Security, Defence & Law Enforcement
Includes police and security studies, criminology, emergency services and security operations.

ACCOUNTANCY, FINANCE & INSURANCE

Accountancy & Taxation
Includes subjects such as accountancy, business studies, taxation, payroll and accounting technician preparation studies.

Banking & Financial Services
Includes financial and legal services studies, office IT skills and frontline financial services studies

Insurance
Includes subjects such as business administration, office IT skills, business and insurance studies.

BUSINESS, SALES & TOURISM

Advertising, Marketing & Public Relations
Includes marketing, business management, advertising and promotion, public relations (PR), and event management.

Business Management & Human Resources
Includes business practice, business administration, e-business and commerce, business IT and management.

Clerical & Administration
Includes secretarial studies, computer applications, office administration, European computer driving licence (ECDL), legal executive, and computerised accounts.

Sales, Retail & Purchasing
Includes customer service, retail practice, sales and marketing, buying and merchandising, advertising and promotion, and retail management.

Tourism & Hospitality
Includes tourism studies, information technology, hotel management, hospitality studies, airline and travel studies.

Transport & Logistics
Includes subjects relating to the transportation of goods and people, such as warehousing skills, logistics and distribution and fleet management.

Area most interested in...   *Second most interested area...*   *Third most interested area...*

1_____   2_____   3_____

Exercise: #2. Consider All Factors

Each course and college you consider offers different opportunities. Read through the items below and decide which aspects of a course are most important to you.

a) In the first column (**A**) place a ✓ in the box if the item is important to you, or place an ✗ if it is not important.

b) Add your own factors at the end and mark them in the same way.

c) In the second column (**B**), number the items you have ticked, giving a 1 to the factor that is most important, 2 the second most important and so on. This should help you to establish your priorities in a course.

d) Fill in the **Priority Grid** on the right with the priorities you just established. These grids are helpful tools which let you compare courses based on what's important to you. With your priorities written in you are ready to start adding some of the courses in which you are most interested, and see if they meet your priorities (see Exercise #3, page 162).

 Course Content:
The material on this course is exactly what I want to study. Give this a Star Rating based on how well the subject matches your interests.

A   B

Career Focused:
I am pursuing a certain career or industry sector, and a course which leads me directly to what I'm looking for.

Broad Subject Areas:
I am not sure what to focus on yet, so I want a course offering a broad introduction to an area that will allow me to specialise when I understand more.

College Facilities:
The course I'm studying should have excellent academic and practical facilities to improve my learning experience.

Links to 3rd Level Education:
The course contains particular modules which are recognised for follow-on study at Level 6 or higher

Good Employment Potential:
I want a course which has a high rate of success in placing students in full time employment when the course finishes.

Freedom:
I would like the opportunity to live away from home and manage my own life.

Work Experience:
I want a course that offers a good choice of work experience options.

Additional Qualifications:
In addition to a QQI Level 5 or 6 qualification I will get an additional recognised qualification (e.g.: ACCA, City & Guilds etc.)

Links with colleges overseas:
The course offers the opportunity for me to progress to further studies in my subject area of interest in a college overseas.

Social Life:
I would like to study in a college with a reputation for an active social life and activities which suit my interests.

Other Factor:_____

Description:_____

Other Factor:_____

Description:_____

Exercise: #3. Research

In the previous exercises you identified how to search for courses and what to look for when you find them. In this exercise you go online and use the search criteria you choose in Exercise #1 to generate a list of courses. You then start to evaluate them according to your requirements set out in Exercise #2. You can do this using the **PLC - FET Choices App** online, or you can complete it here using college prospectuses and the **Priority Grids** provided on the next pages.

Online Version

Login to your **Reach⁺** Career File, select the **World of Education** tab and select the **PLC & FET Choices App.** Follow the Steps shown in the App as follows:

1. **Deciding Whats' Important**: Enter your choices from Exercise #2
2. **Find & Tag**: Use our CourseFinder tool and enter your selections from Exercise #1. If you like a course, 'tag' it [⭐]. Use other filters on the CourseFinder if required.
3. **Research & Evaluate**: The courses you tagged will now be listed ready to be researched in detail, with links to all the information you need provided. For each course, select the Evaluate option and record your findings.
4. **Rank & Save**: Review your choices and arrange the list by dragging your top preferences to the top.

Book Version

a) Fill in the top of the **Priority Grids** with the selections you made in Exercise #2.
b) Using prospectuses from the colleges you are interested in, find courses relating to the Career Sectors you selected in Exercise #1.
c) Enter the college and title into the Grids on the next page.
d) Rate the course content from 1 - 5 by shading the stars, based on the information you read about the course.
e) Place a tick in the Grid where the college/course satisfies the 'Factors' that matter to you.
f) Repeat steps **c - e** for as many courses that interest you.

Example of completed Priority Grid:

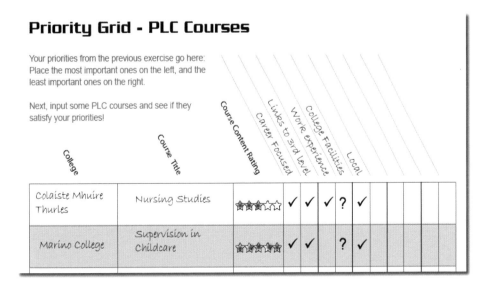

Priority Grid - PLC Courses

Your priorities from Exercise #2 go here: Place the most important ones on the left, and the least important ones on the right.

Next, input some PLC courses and see if they satisfy your priorities!

College	Course Title	Course Content Rating									
		☆☆☆☆☆									
		☆☆☆☆☆									
		☆☆☆☆☆									
		☆☆☆☆☆									
		☆☆☆☆☆									
		☆☆☆☆☆									
		☆☆☆☆☆									
		☆☆☆☆☆									
		☆☆☆☆☆									
		☆☆☆☆☆									
		☆☆☆☆☆									
		☆☆☆☆☆									
		☆☆☆☆☆									

Signature ✎

#4. Results

+ | add to **Career Portfolio**

Review the information in your PLC Priority Grid. The information you gathered should help guide you to make a decision on which courses will suit you best. Generally, the more stars you fill and ticks you have given on the left side of the grid, the closer the course matches your preferences. However, as you go through this exercise you may discover that you need more information, or that other items need to be considered. These can be added to your Grid and researched further.

Overview of education and training options after school

There are many alternatives to choosing PLC or CAO courses straight from school. Consider the various education and training routes below when choosing your future options.

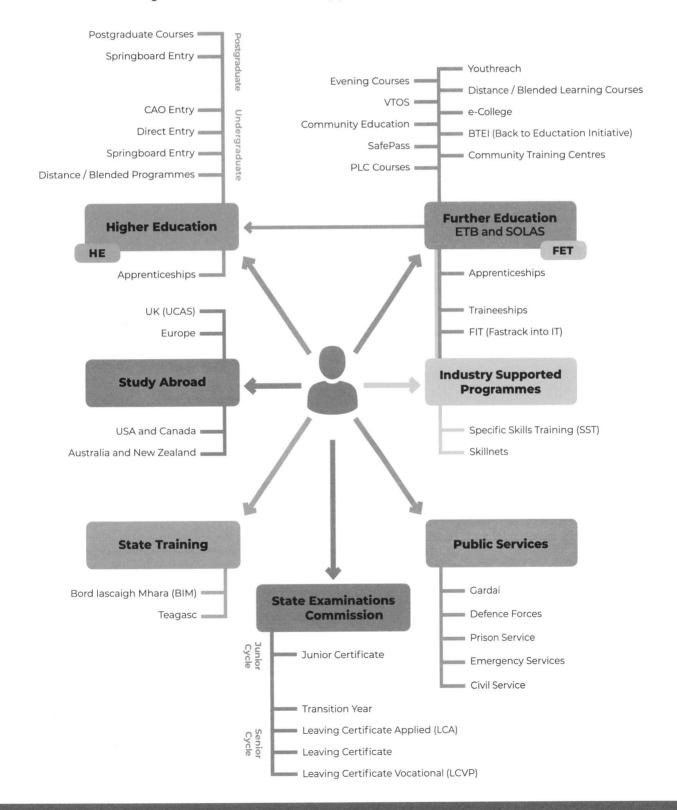

PLC Progression Routes

Using a Post Leaving Certificate (PLC) Course to Access Higher Education

Most students going on to Higher Education use their Leaving Cert results to secure a place in college, but there is another way – the PLC route. Often called a 'back door' route, it relies on your PLC course results instead. This involves taking a PLC course (one that offers a QQI award) after school, and then using the results from that to apply to college. Not all PLC courses lead to QQI awards - some lead to Edexcel or City & Guilds awards, which are increasingly offering similar progression opportunities.

This way may take an extra year compared to the straight 'Leaving Cert' route to get a Degree, but it offers the chance (not a guarantee, unfortunately!) to get a course you really want if the Leaving Certificate lets you down. Thousands of students each year take this route – so here is how it works:

Exercise: Finding a PLC course with Higher Education links

If you are choosing a PLC course for the purpose of getting into college, then first select the college course you want, and check if this route is possible.

How to find PLC courses with Higher Education links:

1. Login to your **Reach⁺** Career File
2. Choose the **World of Education** tab
3. Select the **CourseFinder Tool**. Use the filters to generate a list of CAO (Higher Education) courses that interest you.
4. Select a course that shows that it has a QQI Link, and click on it to show the course details.
5. Look for the QQI / FET Links information. The course may accept **Any** QQI award, or it may accept only certain Major Awards, which will be listed. Note any **Essential Module Requirements** listed, as these will be required as part of your course.
6. Click on each of the **QQI course codes** shown, or the **View Courses** link to view a list of eligible courses.
7. Tag [⭐] any courses you are interested in to save these to your Career File.

> **Important Note:** Some Higher Education links may exist that are not published. You need to contact the Higher Education college directly for information about any links to specific courses that interest you.

If there is a Higher Education link available, then taking this route is possible. You will be competing for a limited number of places, so how well you do in your course matters (see Understanding Points, next page). You may also need to satisfy particular course requirements set out by the college (e.g. achieving a certain number of distinctions, or getting a distinction in certain modules). Look out for this information in the course details page online, or in the college prospectus.

Using your QQI award to select courses through the CAO

Many students undertake a PLC course without intending to continue to Higher Education. However, once you have a QQI award, it may be worth exploring what Higher Education options may be available to you. Almost 1,000 CAO courses are available to PLC students presenting with any QQI Level 5 or 6 award, and many more are available with specific awards!

Exercise: Finding CAO courses that accept specific QQI awards

The following example will show you the steps required to find CAO courses that will accept the QQI award 5M2468 (Business Administration) as an entry requirement (choose a different code if you prefer).

1. Login to your **Reach**[+] Career File.
2. Choose the **World of Education** tab
3. Select the **Progression Routes Tool.**
4. Note that all of the courses first listed will accept **ANY** QQI award. Additional courses not on this first list will show when a specific course is entered into the search.
5. Choose 5M2468 (or your code) from the QQI award field and click on the **Search** button.
6. A list of the additional eligible courses is shown. Use the **Career Sector** and **Location** filters to narrow down your results.
7. Click on the **Course Titles** to view details about the course
8. Look at the **QQI / FET Links** information on the course page and note any **Essential Module Requirements**.
9. Tag [★] any courses you are interested in to save these to your Career File.

Understanding Points

If you use a QQI award (at Level 5 or 6) to enter Higher Education, the success of your application will depend on your results. Just like the Leaving Cert, your results will be converted to CAO points, and colleges will accept the applicants with the highest points. Below, you can see the differences between Leaving Cert and PLC awards:

	Leaving Cert	**PLC**
Study Topics:	'Subjects'	'Modules'
Grades:	H1, O2, etc.	Pass, Merit, Distinction
Results:	Top 6 Subjects	Top 8 Modules*
Maximum Score:	625 Points	390 Points

*Credits Vs Points:

In most Further and Higher Education courses, every module you take has a credit value. Short modules have fewer credits than longer modules. Completing a module means you have achieved all the credits for that module. Typically, PLC modules are 15 credits each – so completing 8 modules = 120 credits. 120 Credits are needed to achieve a QQI Major award.

However, sometimes a module will have as much as 30 credits, so completing one large module (30 Credits) plus 6 more normal modules (6 × 15 = 90) would achieve the 120 credits needed. Some courses also offer additional modules, in which case you use the scores from your best ones to calculate your points, but this makes figuring out your points trickier.

The calculation of points from QQI awards is challenging – especially if not all modules undertaken have 15 credits each. We strongly recommend using the **QQI Points Calculator Tool** available in the **World of Education** tab of your **Reach⁺** Career File to convert your results into points.

A typical QQI results certificate will show a list of modules and the grade (Distinction, Merit, Pass) achieved. Also included is the number of credits for each module, as this is needed to calculate your points.

If you can't access the online calculator, and all your modules are worth 15 credits, it's possible to manually calculate your points by following the instructions below:

> **How to manually calculate Points (calculator recommended!):**
> If all modules are worth *exactly* 15 credits:
> • For each *Distinction*, score 48.75 points.
> • For each *Merit*, score 32.5 points.
> • For each *Pass*, score 16.25 points.
> The total score is an approximation of your points.
>
> Scores are correct at time of print, but subject to change. Latest data can be found online in our QQI Points Calculator.

Exercise: Further Education Progression Routes

Mary has just completed a course in Multimedia Production at Kinsale College of Further Education. The course leads to the QQI Major award 5M2146 at Level 5. She has achieved 3 Distinctions and has passed all other modules. She also has a pass in Maths in the Leaving Cert. Find two Higher Education courses for which she is eligible.

Course #1: _____

Course #2: _____

Mary may be eligible for these courses, but a course offer will be based on her points score as well. Calculate her approximate points based on the results she obtained as follows:

Module Code:	Module Name:	Credits:	Grade:	Points:
5N1299:	Multimedia Authoring	15	Distinction	
5N1300:	Multimedia Project Development	15	Merit	
5N0784:	Design Skills	15	Merit	
5N0690:	Communications	15	Distinction	
5N1356:	Work Experience	15	Merit	
5N1603:	Computer 3D Modelling & Animation	15	Pass	
5N1605:	Digital Movie Processing	15	Merit	
5N1978:	Graphic Design Skills	15	Distinction	
			Total:	

Apprenticeships

Apprenticeships are a type of training designed to prepare students for a range of occupations using a combination of college study and workplace employment. Unlike most CAO & PLC courses, apprenticeships require you to find a company to employ you while you are doing your course, and you then spend half of your time learning on the job with your employer, and the other half in college. One of the best parts is you get paid while you are learning – so you are earning money all the time!

Apprenticeships are regarded as one of the best ways to learn complex skills. Most apprenticeships can be found in the following general career areas, with new areas being added all of the time. A full list is available in your **Reach⁺** Career File.

- Agriculture, Animals & Food
- Science, Engineering & Construction
- Accountancy, Finance & Insurance
- Business, Sales & Tourism

To explore Apprenticeship opportunities:
1. Login to your **Reach⁺** Career File.
2. Open the World of Work tab
3. Click on the **Apprenticeships Tool**

Exercise: Apprenticeship Investigation

Apprenticeship Name: _____

College: _____ Qualification Level NFQ: _____

Colour Vision Test Required: _____ Apprenticeship Duration: _____

Student Contribution Fee: _____

Entry Requirements: _____

_____

_____

What elements of this apprenticeship would you find to be the most engaging / interesting, and why?

_____

_____

_____

_____

_____

What would you find to be challenging about this apprenticeship, and why? _____

_____

_____

_____

How do you become an apprentice? _____

_____

_____

Course Investigation

Gaining as much information as possible on a course prior to applying is very important. Fill in this form for each course you are considering applying for. Download copies of this page as often as needed from your **Reach⁺** Career File, or complete the form online.

Course Name: _____   Code: _____

College: _____   Number of Places: _____

Qualification(s): _____   Course Duration: _____

Where to apply: _____   Fees: _____

Entry Requirements: _____

Which subjects in this course are you attracted to? _____

_____

_____

_____

Which subjects in this course are you least attracted to? _____

_____

_____

_____

What careers or further progression routes might this course lead you to? _____

_____

_____

_____

What additional information about this course have you found from anyone involved in it? (from someone who has done it, is doing it, or works for the college?) _____

_____

_____

_____

What other similar courses are available? _____

_____

_____

_____

Why I would choose/not choose this course? _____

_____

_____

_____

Useful Resources: www.careersportal.ie • www.qualifax.ie • www.cao.ie • College websites

The World of Work

Exercise: Not a lot to ask?

> *They weren't asking for much...*
> *A weekend, a holiday, just a bit more time with their families*
> *For women to be treated equally, a better retirement...*
> *Not much, just a fair chance.*
> *They were our parents, and their parents.*
> *They were hard working, tough, and resilient*
> *But knew that together they were bigger than the sum of their individual ambitions.*
> *They had a vision. To make the world just that little bit better.*
> *And together they did, in so many ways.*
> *We now have paid annual leave, 4 weeks holiday...*
> *Not a lot to ask.*
> *Together these men and women secured our rights at work, fair pay and conditions...*
> *So we can all look forward to a more balanced lifestyle, and a comfortable retirement.*
> *It was their work that led to maternity leave, equal rights, jobseeker benefits.*
> *They struggled for a life outside work, the eight hour day, the weekend free,*
> *And they still try to find enough time for their families and friends.*
> *Yes, there is more to do.*
> *And now it's our turn.*
> *Together we need to face the new world of work...*
> *The challenges of the new global workplace.*
> *We must accept human differences,*
> *In race, beliefs, work practices and values.*
> *We need to ensure that everyone is to be treated equally – whoever they are.*
> *We must learn what needs to be learned,*
> *Change what needs to be changed, and make our country,*
> *And the world that little bit better...*
> *For our future, our children, and our planet...*
> *Piece by piece,*
> *Not a lot to ask.*

The world of work that you will enter into has been shaped by those who have gone before you. What benefits do you expect to enjoy when you enter the workforce?

_____

_____

_____

_____

Which of these benefits is most important to you? Why? _____

_____

_____

_____

Is there anything wrong with the workplace today? How might you go about making changes? _____

_____

_____

_____

Exercise: Why do people work?

+ | add to **Career Portfolio**

Read through the following list of reasons people have given for working. Are any of these reasons important for you? Rate each item according to how important this would be for your ideal work. You can add your own reasons in the blank spaces provided.

Work Satisfiers	Low	–			High
	1	2	3	4	5
1. Keeps me busy and helps fill in time					
2. Lets me help people					
3. Allows me to be with others					
4. Offers me chances for improvement and/or promotion					
5. Gives me power/influence over others					
6. Allows me to contribute to the community					
7. Lets me experience new things and learn more					
8. Lets me control my own time					
9. Allows me to be known and liked by many people					
10. Allows me to be responsible					
11. Allows me to meet a lot of people					
12. Provides opportunities to make friends					
13. Lets me use my special abilities, skills and knowledge					
14. Allows me to satisfy my other needs					
15. Provides money					
16. Provides physical activity for me					
17. Lets me be creative					
18. Makes me feel that I'm doing something useful					
19. Involves doing a variety of tasks					
20. Lets me see something for my efforts					
21.					
22.					

Which three reasons would be the most important to you?

#1. _____

#2. _____

#3. _____

Choose one of these reasons and explain why it is important to you.

_____

_____

_____

_____

Which three reasons are the most important in your class?

#1. _____

#2. _____

#3. _____

The Generation Gap(s)

When you enter the world of work, you may find that there are people of all ages working in the same company. This has many benefits: the years of experience which older employees can offer is invaluable, while younger employees are more familiar with changing trends and technology.

However, growing up in a different time period can have a strong influence on how people behave, what they value, and what they expect from their co-workers. This can lead to misunderstandings and conflict in the workplace; simply because people don't know how to deal with other generations.

Management professionals (who usually end up having to resolve these problems) have done a lot of research into how to help workers of different ages to cooperate. They divide people into five 'generations', with distinct attitudes, behaviours, and expectations.

These are, of course, broad stereotypes, and should not be applied to all individuals born in these timeframes. The goal of this introduction is to prepare you to communicate with people of different generations when you enter the workplace, such as knowing how to take instruction, when it is appropriate to be casual, how to approach deadlines, and so on.

The Veterans: (born before 1945)

The veterans are the oldest generation in the workplace. They are very socially and financially conservative. They may fear that they will be replaced by younger generations, particularly because they are technologically weak. Many are still in the workforce because they enjoy working, and some are just there for financial reasons. Their life experience gives them a lot to offer.

Baby Boomers (born 1946– 1960)

Baby Boomers are now one of the older generations at work. They were born during the booming, optimistic times post World War II. They value hard work and long hours as the means to success and thus work ethic is extremely important to them. They are competitive and goal-oriented, and aim to achieve.

Generation X (born 1961 – 1980)

Generation X is the middle generation. They were raised by Baby Boomers who worked long hours, and were the first generation to experience significant marital breakdown and separation. As a result, "Generation Xers" tend to be very independent and flexible, and dislike rigid schedules and formal workplaces. They are also the first generation to grow up with digital technology, and are comfortable with using it.

Generation Y / Millennials (born 1981 – 1995)

Generation Y is strongly associated with technology, multitasking, and being highly educated. Raised by parents who did not want to make the mistakes of the previous generation, Generation Y is confident, ambitious, and expects to achieve. Long working hours have lost priority to time spent on entertainment, and with friends and family.

Generation Z / iGen (born 1996– 2010)

Generation Z (that's you!) are more self-aware, self-reliant, innovative and goal-oriented than Gen Y. They are more eco-aware, more able to learn for themselves (YouTube / Pinterest), and place a priority on how fast you can find the right information rather than on whether or not you know the right information. Being 'connected' is taken for granted - how could it be otherwise?

Exercise: Future Generations

The following table lists some of the 'typical' differences between the five generations currently in the work place. Much of this information has been gathered by researchers in America, and adapted for the Irish experience. The Birth Dates are approximate - as are some of the names!

Take a look at the characteristics of existing generations. Then complete the table with your predictions for how the next generation (born 2010+) might be characterised in the space provided. What should this new generation be called?

	Veterans	Baby Boomers	Generation X
Birth Date:	1925-1945	1946-1960	1961-1980
Defining Events:	WW1, WW2, The Great Depression	Cold War, Civil Rights Movement	Northern Ireland Conflict, EU, AIDS,
Entertainment:	Radio, Newspaper, Cinema	TV (2 channels), Comic books, Vinyl	TV (8+ channels), VCR, Nintendo, SEGA, Atari, Cassette tapes
Expected Education:	Primary School	Leaving Certificate	College Degree
View of Authority:	Honour and respect for Church and State leaders	Question leaders	Challenge state leaders, ignore church leaders
Managing Money:	Save	Spend	Invest
Messages which Motivate:	"Your experience is respected here" "Your perseverance will be rewarded"	"We recognise your unique and important contribution to our team" "What is your vision for this project?"	"Whatever you think is best" "There aren't a lot of rules here" "We've got the newest hardware and software"
Feedback:	No news is good news.	Once a year, with lots of documentation.	"Sorry to interrupt, but how am I doing?"
Successful Because:	Fought hard and won it	Ambitious and dedicated to career	Adaptable
Characteristics:	Hardworking, Dependable, Loyal to employer, Private	Educated, Independent, Questions authority,	Sceptical, Self Sufficient, Serious, Tolerant,
Values:	Dedication, Conformity, Authority, Patience, Duty	Optimism, Involvement, Personal growth	Diversity, Informality, Pragmatism, Self Reliance
Sayings:	No sweat	No problem	No bother
Social Communications:	Handwritten letters, Visits, Telegraph	Cars, Touch tone phones	Commercial flight, Landline
Fashions:	Formal	Less rigid	Casual
Employment:	A means of survival; One job for life	Central focus; a few jobs, emigration	Annoying but necessary; jobs becoming more plentiful

Reach+

TRADS 1928 – 1944

TRADITIONALISTS:
Value authority and a top-down management approach; hard working; 'make do or do without'.

BOOMERS 1945 – 1964

BABY BOOMERS:
Expect some degree of deference to their opinions; workaholics

GEN X 1965 – 1979

GENERATION X:
Comfortable with authority; will work as hard as is needed; importance of work life balance.

GEN Y 1980 – 1994

GENERATION Y:
Respect must be earned. Technologically savvy; goal and achievement oriented.

GEN Z 1995+

GENERATION Z:
Many traits still to emerge. Digital natives, fast decision makers, highly connected.

Generation Y	Generation Z	?
1981-1995	1996 - 2010	
9/11 Good Friday Agreement	Arab Spring War on Terror; Brexit	
Internet, Playstation, TV (120+ channels), DVD, Streaming video	YouTube, Instagram Spotify, Netflix	
Lifelong Learning	Non-Linear, Virtual Classroom	
Respect leaders, but not worship them.	Lead - but don't Micromanage	
Spend parents' money	Save	
"You'll be working with bright, creative people"	"Make a difference" "Work to live, not live to work" "What do you think?"	
Whenever anyone wants it, at the touch of a button.	Likes mentorship, In-person praise	
Determination	[not known yet!]	
Ambitious, Team-oriented, Educated, Confident,	Connected, Resourceful, Creative, Pragmatic	
Sociability, Diversity, Confidence, Morality,	Social Justice, Activism, Connectivity, Free Information	
No	lol	
Email, Social Networking, Mobile Phones, Internet	Facetime, Snapchat, Facebook, Instragram	
Anything goes	Individuality	
Adaptive, frequent moving between jobs.	Portfolio Careers, Many Jobs, More Entrepreneurial	

Career Sectors

The world of work can be divided up into a number of groupings or sectors, each having something in common, such as their role and function within the economy, or the types of occupations that characterise it. Very often people are attracted to the type of products made or the services provided by a particular sector, and seek to build a career in that area.

Exploring career sectors is an excellent starting point when looking to find a career direction. You may find that a particular occupation interests you most now, only to find that as you explore related occupations in the same general area, a more interesting one catches your attention.

Many sectors undergo a lot of changes as they grow and contract over time according to local and international demand. Being aware of what influences the development of the sectors that interest you most will prepare you to take advantage of the best opportunities that arise.

www.careersportal.ie

Reach+

Exercise: Career Sectors

Sectors in the Economy

The Irish Government has been forced to call a general election. A group of politicians visit your school and plead with you and your classmates to get involved in politics and run in the general election. Although politics may not be 'your thing', encouraged by your friends you reluctantly agree to run for election.

To your utter surprise and shock, you get elected.

The new Government is anxious that more young people get involved in running the country. You have been invited to a meeting. Before the meeting you have been sent a list of the sectors in the Irish economy. You have been asked to select the sectors that you would most like to work with while you are in government.

These will be sectors that you are interested in and believe that you can help grow, improve and develop. You are promised that you will be assigned a ministry post in charge of one of the sectors from your four favorites.

On the next page, you can review the sectors and select the sectors that interest you most.

Career Sectors

Read through each of the following career sectors. Place a tick ✓ in the boxes next to those sectors that interest you (column A). When finished, review the sectors you ticked, and place the number 1 beside the sector you are most interested in (in column B to the right of the tick boxes). Then place the number 2 beside the sector you are next interested in, and so on until you have selected your top four sectors.

A B

Accountancy & Taxation
Working mainly in business, records details of financial transactions and provides advice on financial and tax matters.

Advertising, Marketing & Public Relations
Creating advertising, managing marketing campaigns, and ensuring that a company is always seen in the best possible light.

Animals & Veterinary Science
Looking after the health and welfare of animals.

Art, Craft & Design
Producing new pieces of art, craft or design work.

Banking & Financial Services
Providing services to the public and business through banking, fund management and other forms of financial services.

Biological, Chemical & Pharmaceutical Science
Creating high quality drugs or chemicals, testing them to ensure they are effective and safe, and monitoring their effect on people and the environment.

Biomedical Technologies & Medtech
Work on the development of technology that enhances the diagnosis, prevention, monitoring, and treatment of diseases and disabilities.

Business Management & Human Resources
Involved in the running of a business, helping it grow and develop, operate efficiently, meet business objectives and manage its workforce.

Clerical & Administration
Working in an office and being involved in the day to day running of a business.

Community & Voluntary
Working to provide services to people of all ages across areas including social, community, youth, education, and charity, voluntary and sporting organisations.

Computers & ICT
Working in the manufacture, sales or support of all forms of computers and computer systems, or in the creation and development of software.

Construction, Architecture & Property
Working in the planning, building, selling or management of construction projects (housing estates, roads, warehouses etc.).

Earth & Environment
Work with technologies which monitor and predict changes in our environment, the development of renewable energy sources, and the conservation of ecosystems.

Education
Teaching at any level, including professional training, or involved in the design and development of courses and the qualifications that they lead to.

Engineering, Manufacturing and Energy
Working in one of the many engineering or technology fields such as Civil, Mechanical, Electrical, Manufacturing, Motor and Energy.

	A	**B**

Farming, Horticulture & Forestry
Working with the land, managing livestock, crops, forests or the environment. □ ___

Fashion & Beauty
Working in any area involving fashion, beauty care, hairdressing and personal hygiene, e.g. Fashion design, Beauty therapy etc. □ ___

Food & Beverages
Working with the production, distribution, preparation and serving of food and drinks. □ ___

Government, Politics and EU
Working for the government to ensure the efficient and correct running of the country. □ ___

Healthcare
Working in hospitals, clinics and medical centres looking after the health and care of people with physical illness. □ ___

History, Culture & Languages
Working in museums, art galleries or heritage management, or using languages professionally, e.g. translating or interpreting. □ ___

Insurance
Providing and selling insurance services to the public and businesses. □ ___

Law & Legal
Involved in the administration of the law, defending the rights of individuals and organisations. □ ___

Leisure, Sport & Fitness
Working in a leisure centre, in sports as a player or coach, or involved in personal / fitness training. □ ___

Maritime, Fishing & Aqua-culture
Fishing in the open seas or farming them in fish farms. Looking after the sale and promotion of all seafood. □ ___

Media, Film & Publishing
Communicating information through various forms of media, e.g. TV, Radio, newspapers, the internet, and film. □ ___

Music & Performing Arts
Working in the music/entertainment business as an artist (performer) or in one of the many roles that are involved in the design and production of a show. □ ___

Physics, Mathematics & Space Science
Researching and investigating aspects of the physical universe, or using mathematics to solve complex issues in science or business. □ ___

Psychology & Social Care
Caring for individuals experiencing psychological difficulties, or with the welfare of individuals or groups of people experiencing some form of hardship. □ ___

Sales, Retail & Purchasing
All forms of work directly involved in the delivery of products and services to the marketplace. □ ___

Security, Defence & Law Enforcement
Working in the Garda, Army, Navy, Air Corps, or other organisations involved in personal, national or cyber security. □ ___

Tourism & Hospitality
Attending to the needs of local and visiting tourists, e.g. the hotels, restaurants, bars and tourist attractions, and promoting Ireland as a welcoming place to visit. □ ___

Transport & Logistics
Transporting goods and people, the infrastructure (roads, rail etc.) that make this possible, and the services that are required to maintain operations 24/7. □ ___

My Career Sectors

+ add to **Career Portfolio**

Enter the names of the four sectors which interest you the most:

Most interesting Sectors:

1. _____
2. _____
3. _____
4. _____

Country in Crisis

You have been awarded a ministerial post in one of your most preferred sectors. You are now a Government minister. Unfortunately, only weeks after the new government was elected, there is an economic crash! The country is in trouble and the new government needs to take urgent action to reduce its spending.

The Taoiseach has called all the ministers together and has asked that they report back to explain at a government meeting why their sector is important for Ireland. Your task is to defend your sector from cutbacks and put a case together for increased expenditure.

> **Note:** Start your research by accessing the **Career Sectors Tool** from the **World Of Work** tab of your **Reach⁺** Career File.

For the purpose of this exercise, assume you were given a ministerial post in a sector you would like to explore. Prepare your case using the following form:

Exercise: Sector Investigation

Sector Name: _____

Brief Description of this Sector: _____

_____

_____

_____

Occupations which characterise this sector: _____

_____

_____

What this sector contributes to society: _____

_____

_____

Reach⁺

Examples of businesses operating in this sector: _____

_____

_____

_____

_____

_____

_____

Employment trends (e.g. changes, improving or declining): _____

_____

_____

_____

_____

_____

Why this sector should receive more funding: _____

_____

_____

_____

_____

_____

_____

_____

Why does this sector appeal to you? _____

_____

_____

_____

_____

_____

Other notes and comments: _____

_____

_____

_____

_____

_____

Career Investigation

Career Investigated: _____

Describe this career:

[e.g. the type of work the person would be doing, the main tasks and responsibilities]

_____

_____

_____

_____

_____

What are the most important skills for the job?

[e.g. communication skills / IT skills / social skills / practical skills / numerical skills / problem solving skills etc.]

_____

_____

_____

_____

What are the most important personal qualities or attributes required for this position?

[what personality characteristics, interests and aptitudes are needed]

_____

_____

_____

_____

Identify 2 different courses that may lead to this career:

Course Name & Code: _____

College Name: _____

Course Entry Requirements: _____

[e.g. Minimum Irish: O6, English: O6, Mathematics: H5]

Admission Procedure: _____

[e.g. through CAO. Last years points were 360]

Course duration: _____

[e.g. 3 years full-time]

Qualification awarded: _____

[e.g. Degree - Honours Bachelor (Level 8 NFQ) from NUI]

Course Name & Code: _____

College Name: _____

Course Entry Requirements: _____

[e.g. Minimum Irish: O6, English: O6, Mathematics: H5]

Admission Procedure: _____

[e.g. through CAO. Last years points were 360]

Course duration: _____

[e.g. 3 years full-time]

Qualification awarded: _____

[e.g. Degree - Honours Bachelor (Level 8 NFQ) from NUI]

Discuss this career in terms of your personal aptitude and interests:

[how well do your personal aptitudes and interests match what is needed for the job?]

_____

_____

_____

_____

_____

_____

Discuss this career in terms of the subjects you are studying for in the Leaving Cert:

[how relevant are your subjects in terms of preparing you for this career, or courses required for this career?]

_____

_____

_____

_____

_____

_____

Note three things you discovered about this career that you would regard as advantages:

_____

_____

_____

_____

_____

Note three things you discovered about this career that you would regard as disadvantages:

_____

_____

_____

_____

_____

What other careers would you now consider worthwhile investigating?

_____

_____

Resources used for this investigation:

[List any books, articles, websites, interviews etc., taken during the course of this investigation]

_____

_____

_____

_____

Work Experience

+ | add to **Career Portfolio**

Work experience is a great opportunity to find out about what sort of work you might enjoy, and to learn about the skills you need to succeed in the workplace. It can help you to decide what you want to do after school, what you would like to find out more about, and what is most definitely not for you!

Finding a placement

Your work placement is supposed to be an introduction to the world of work, and does not have to be a career path that you are planning to continue with. Aim for an area of work which you'd like to learn more about, or one which you find interesting. Below are some tips on finding a suitable work placement:

» Ask your family and relatives if they know anyone who works in an industry in which you are interested, and see if they can get you a placement.

» Use the **Work Placements Tool** in the **World of Work** tab of your **Reach⁺** Career File to search for placements advertised online.

» Your school may have some links with local companies who are willing to offer work placements, so consult your Guidance Counsellor about any availabilities.

» Start asking early! Having a placement booked well in advance will save you from ending up in a placement you didn't want and possibly won't enjoy.

Fill in some Career Sectors and/or companies that interest you below, to get you started:

Target Sectors:	Target Companies:

Making an application for work experience

Whether you are making application by phone call, letter, online or in person, make sure to include the points below in any communication. If writing, it may be useful to phone initially to find out to whom a letter of application should be addressed, so that it reaches the right person and you know who to follow up with at a later date. Also, some large companies have application forms and closing dates for accepting applications which you can find out about with a phone call. You should include:

✔ Your name
✔ Your school
✔ Your school year
✔ The reason you are making contact, i.e. enquiring about work experience opportunities
✔ The dates you are seeking a placement
✔ Your contact details
✔ A copy of your CV

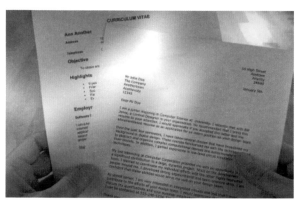

> **Note:** You can use the **TY Work Experience App** in the **World of Work** tab, or the **Diary of Work Experience App** in the **LCVP** tab to complete a work experience report.

Curriculum Vitae

Sales Assistant Wanted
For Busy Supermarket

We are a rapidly expanding company currently operating 15 Irish and UK stores, 3 European stores, and 7 US stores.

The person we are seeking should be an outgoing, self motivated person with good communication skills. Willingness to show initiative and a desire to progress their career with us would be desirable.

To apply, e-mail your CV to
recruitment@busyfriendlycheapsupermarket.ie
by 28th January

The above advertisement was displayed in a busy city suburb characterised by a multicultural population. The Human Resources Manager received a number of applications, and has narrowed the selection to two applicants. On the pages that follow, the CVs of the two possible candidates are reproduced.

Read down through the CVs and evaluate the two candidates' suitability for the position as advertised. Once you have made up your mind, fill in the answers to the questions in the exercise that follows.

Curriculum Vitae of Teresa Foreman

Date of Birth: 18th of October 2002   Address: 20 Broadfield Close,
Kilmacan Rd.
Woodbrook
Dublin 12
Phone: (01) 487295

Education:

St Patrick Junior Primary School,
Woodbrook   2007 - 2011

St Paticks Senior Primary School
Woodbrook   2010 - 2016

Grange Park Community School
Dublin Rd. Woodbrook   2016 - 2021

Examinations:

Junior Certificate   **2018.**
6 Honours: c English, b history, A Maths, C Science, C Wood Tech.,
C Music
4 Passes: D Geography, D Irish, D French, E Business

Leaving Cert
Honours: English H3, History H6, Art H2, Business H6
Pass: Maths O2, Chemstry O3, Irish O3

Transition Year: Transition Year   2018 - 2019

Work experience: St Paul Primary School Woodbrook   Transition Year 2018
Top Twenty Music Shop, Woodbrook   TY 2019

Specials:

Music project - Percussion - Late Late Show Audition   Spring 2017
Production of records in school and music studio   TY Nov 2018
Art project - Art exhibition in City Centre Arts Centre   TY January 2019
Weekly 1 hour voluntary work: Teaching young children to read in St Paul
Primary School , Sutton, Co Dublin   TY Feb to June 2019

Interest and Hobbies:

Active Member of Woodbrook Musical Society   2014 - 2017
Active member of comunity band playing Percussion   2015/16
Computers (Art / desktop publishing) course   July 2020 -
Cycling   2019 -

Referees:

Peter Gallagher   Sharon Murphy,
Principal   Group Leader,
Woodbrook Community Band   Grange Park Community College
4 Malborough Park,   Dublin 12.
Dublin 12.   Ph. 01- 786104
Ph: 01 - 713751

Curriculum Vitae

Personal Details:

Name: Barski Romari   Nationality: Polish

Date of Birth: 26 /5/ 2004   Phone: 045 87595

Address: 25 The Paddocks,   Gender: Male
Newbridge,
Co. Kildare

Education:

Primary School: St Aiden's Primary School, Newbridge, Co. Kildare

Secondary School: St Josephs College, Newbridge, Co. Kildare

Examination: Irish Junior Certificate Examination, June 2018

Irish: Higher B, English: Higher C, Maths: Higher B. Science: Higher C, Geography: Lower C, Technology: Lower C, Business: Lower A, French: D Lower

Leaving Certificate: June 2021

Maths: Higher H3   Chemistry: Higher H3   Business: Higher H2
Irish: Ordinary O6   Technology: O5   French: Ordinary O5
English: Ordinary O6   Link Modules: Distinction

Achievments: Mini- Company Regional winner, TY year   May 2018
  Student Council   Sept 2018'19
  Student award   May 2021

Work experience: Dunnes Stores, Newbridge   Summer 2019/2020

Hobbies and Interests: Reading, Playing Piano, Soccer, Basketball, Social Work

<u>**Referees:**</u>   James O Rourke
  English Teacher
  St Josephs College,
  Dublin Road
  Co. Dublin

Exercise: Who would you Hire?

From the information presented on the two CVs, who do you think would be best for the job, and why?

_____

_____

_____

_____

_____

_____

_____

_____

_____

The policy of the supermarket is to interview at least two candidates for each position advertised, so both of the above candidates will be called in for an interview. As the interviewer, what questions would you want to ask each candidate to ensure they will be suitable for this position? Consider any details that arise from their CV, but if necessary explore any issues that may not have been included.

Candidate 1

Question:	Why you want to ask this:

Candidate 2

Question:	Why you want to ask this:

Notice: What were your impressions of the two CVs received? Did you notice any spelling mistakes, poor formating, and general lack of quality? Look through the CVs again an spot any mistakes - there are many!

Tips for Writing a CV

General Notes:

- Spelling and punctuation must be perfect: anything less will be considered careless.
- Make sure that you have a clean layout which displays your qualifications, skills and competencies clearly and logically.
- Focus on essential, relevant information which adds value to your application: work experience or training which is old or irrelevant should be excluded.
- Adapt your CV to each job, highlighting your strengths as appropriate to the job you are aiming for.
- Don't bluff: you are likely to be found out during the interview.
- Have an explanation for any breaks in your studies or career.

Layout/Presentation:

- Print your CV on clean white paper.
- Unless you are confident with using your own design, stick to the fonts and layout of the template which you have chosen.
- Don't use ALL CAPS, **bold**, or <u>underline</u> on full sentences: it looks awful.
- Avoid any kind of slang or informal language.
- Don't split an entry under one heading over two pages.

Proofreading:

- Check your CV carefully once you have completed it to remove any spelling mistakes and to ensure that you have included everything you wanted to include.
- Have someone else read your CV before you send it!

*When an employer is first glancing through your CV, they have probably taken it from the middle of a pile with lots of others. To save time, employers will take **any** excuse to bin a CV: a typo, poor formatting, or even irrelevant information is enough to get your CV discarded.*

Sample CVs

The following is a sample of a standard, well constructed CV by a Leaving Certificate Student. Use this as a template from which to make your CV. You can download a copy of this file in Microsoft Word format from within the CV App in your online Career File.

CURRICULUM VITAE

David Lee
15 St Enda's Terrace
Dorset Street, Dublin 7
Tel & Mob numbers

PERSONAL SKILLS/QUALITIES

- Good communication skills
- Organisational ability
- Creative flair and eye for detail
- Customer aware
- Flexible and willing to learn

EDUCATION

Synge Street National School, Dublin 1   2006 - 2014

CBS North Great George's St, Dublin 1   2014 - Present

Junior Certificate 2017

Subject	Level	Grade
English	Higher	C
Irish	Ordinary	D
Maths	Ordinary	B
French	Ordinary	D
History	Higher	C
Geography	Higher	B
Art	Higher	C
Materials Technology Wood	Higher	B
Design & Communication Graphics	Higher	B

Leaving Certificate 2019

Subject	Level	Grade
English	Ordinary	n/a
Irish	Foundation	n/a
Maths	Ordinary	n/a
Technology	Higher	n/a
Design & Communication Graphics	Higher	n/a
Art	Higher	n/a
Link Modules	Common	n/a

WORK EXPERIENCE

Tom Gorman Motors, East Wall Road, Dublin 3   **4 – 8 of March 2018**

Garage Assistant

- Kept main work areas clear and clean
- Ran errands for mechanics
- Dealt with customer queries/orders and accepted payment

                                                                   June – July 2018

Lindsay Motors Ltd, Glasnevin, Dublin 9

Petrol Assistant

- Assisted customers to operate petrol pumps, car wash
- Kept forecourt clean and tidy
- Handled cash/credit card payments

ACHIEVEMENTS

- Represented Dublin City at 200 metres, Community Games, July 2018.
- Captain of U-18 team, Scoil Uí Chonaill GAA club, 2018 - Present.
- School Prefect, September 2018 - Present.

HOBBIES AND INTERESTS

- Art and Drawing, Sport, Music.
- Bass player in school band.

REFEREES

Mr Tom O'Brien
Principal
CBS North Great George's Street
Dublin 1.

Tel: 01-826 3309

Mr Eugene Gaffney
Manager, Tom Gorman Motors Ltd
East Wall Road
Dublin 3.

Tel: 01 853 1211

Date: _____

Signed: _____

PERSONAL INFORMATION

First name(s) / Surname(s):	John Doe
Address(es):	State your complete postal address where you want to be contacted. 12 Yellow Brick Road, Cranmore, Co. Sligo, Ireland
Telephone(s):	Include fixed line and mobile if you have them. 012345678, 087 654 3210
E-mail:	Enter an address suitable for business, such as: johndoe22@gmail.com Avoid casual addresses such as sweetbro666@gmail.com
Nationality(-ies):	Irish
Date of birth:	Use dd/month/yyyy to avoid confusion with American formatting. 25 December 2003

JOB APPLIED FOR

Job Applied For	Enter Job applied for / Position / Preferred job / Studies applied for. This is crucial if you are submitting a CV to a company which is not in response to a job advertisement. Hotel & Tourism, Management

EDUCATION AND TRAINING

Repeat this section for each course which you have undertaken, starting with the most recent.

Dates:	When did the course start and when did it finish? 2015 - 2018		
Title of qualification awarded:	Write the exact title of the qualification awarded: Junior Certificate		
Principal subjects/occupational skills covered:	Summarise the main subjects or occupational skills taught during the course in question, and your achievement level (if appropriate). Include only the last exam taken and provide both subjects and results, e.g.: Junior Certificate:		
	Subject:	Level:	Grade:
	English	Higher	B
	Maths	Higher	C
	Science	Higher	A
	CSPE	Higher	A
	Geography	Higher	B
	Greek	Higher	B
	History	Ordinary	C
	Irish	Ordinary	D
	Spanish	Ordinary	D
Name and type of organisation providing the education:	State the name (and if appropriate, the address) and type of the institution attended: Scoil Mhuire, Letterkenny, Co. Sligo, Ireland		
Qualification level on the National Framework of Qualifications:	Level 3		

PERSONAL INFORMATION

First name(s) / Surname(s):	
Address(es):	
Telephone(s):	
E-mail:	
Nationality:	
Date of birth:	

JOB APPLIED FOR

Job Applied For:	

EDUCATION AND TRAINING

Dates:			
Title of qualification awarded:			
	Junior Certificate:		
Principal subjects/occupational skills covered:	Subject:	Level:	Grade:
Name and type of organisation providing the education:			
Qualification level on the National Framework of Qualifications:			

WORK EXPERIENCE

Dates:	October 2017 to February 2018
Occupation or position held:	Part-time Baby sitting
Main activities and responsibilities:	Looked after two children under age 8. Kept the house tidy. Helped with homework.
Name and address of employer:	If relevant, add additional information such as phone numbers, email, or a homepage. **Mrs Fitzpatrick**, details on request.
Type of business or sector:	State the nature of the employer's business or sector: **Childcare**

PERSONAL SKILLS — Covers skills which are not necessarily covered by formal awards. Remove any sections which are not appropriate to your application.

Mother tongue(s):	**English, Irish**
Other Languages:	State which other languages you have and your level of competence. **German: studying at Leaving Cert level and used on a one month placement in Germany. Earned an A in Junior Certificate German.**
Communication Skills	These refer to living and working with other people, in positions where communication is important and situations where teamwork is essential. **Good communication skills developed during baby-sitting job where I had to discuss how to manage the children with their parents. I also learned to listen and take time to understand the children's needs as they would become difficult if their needs were not met. Excellent team work skills as I am captain of the school hockey team.**
Organisational / managerial skills:	These refer to the coordination and administration of people, projects, and budgets; at work, in voluntary work, etc. **Organising skills and time management skills – developed as captain of hockey team and during baby-sitting job.**
Job-related skills:	These refer to mastery of specific kinds of equipment, machinery, etc. other than computers, or to technical skills and competencies in a specialised field (manufacturing industry, health, banking, etc.). **Learned how to setup and control the lighting system for the school musical using a complicated lighting control board.**
Digital Competence:	Refers to information processing, communications, content creation, safety & problem solving. **Completed ECDL modules in word processing and spreadsheets. Regular user of email, instant messenger and social networks.**
Other skills:	This area is good for mentioning any hobbies, sports, or positions of responsibility in voluntary organisations:. **My hobbies include hockey, writing, cooking, and reading.**
Driving licence(s):	State here whether you hold a driving licence and, if so, for which category of vehicle. For example 'Category B'.
Additional Information:	Include any memberships of professional organisations or community organisations, and references from previous work experience or educational bodies. **References: Mrs Fitzpatrick, details on request. Mr Jones (Team manager), details on request.**

Note:
- Templates for these and other CVs in Microsoft Word format are available from the **CV Builder App** in the **World of Work** tab of your **Reach⁺** Career File

WORK EXPERIENCE

Dates:	
Occupation or position held:	
Main activities and responsibilities:	
Name and address of employer:	
Type of business or sector:	

PERSONAL SKILLS

Mother tongue(s):	
Other Languages:	
Communication skills:	
Organisational / managerial skills:	
Job-related skills:	
Digital Competence:	
Other skills:	
Driving licence(s):	
Additional Information:	

My Career Portfolio

Enter the results of key exercises in this section as you complete them.

Write in your answers/conclusions/suggestions. Shade in the scores from the exercises.

Career Awareness (page 7)	
Something I would like to learn outside of school:	

My Dreams (page 11)	
Past Dreams – Early Primary School	
Past Dreams – Late Primary School	
Past Dreams – Early Secondary School	
Current Dreams:	

What Inspires Me (page 14)	
Who / What 1:	
Who / What 2:	

Dream Your Future (page 15)	
Something remarkable I would like to achieve:	

My Talents (page 16)	
Some of my talents:	

Top Five Values (page 42)	
Life Value 1:	
Life Value 2:	
Life Value 3:	
Life Value 4:	
Life Value 5:	

Personality Quiz (page 44)	5	10	15	20
Improvisor				
Stabiliser				
Theorist				
Idealist				

My Personality Type (page 56):	

Career Interests (page 63)	1	2	3	4	5	6	7
Investigative							
Realistic							
Enterprising							
Linguistic							
Administrative							
Naturalist							
Creative							
Social							

My Career Interests (page 75)

Career suggestions based on my interests:	
CAO Course suggestions based on my interests:	
PLC Course suggestions based on my interests:	

My Aptitudes (page 77)

#1.	
#2.	
#3.	
#4.	
#5.	
#6.	
#7.	
#8.	

My Intelligences (page 83)	5	10	15	20	25	30
Linguistic-Verbal						
Logical-Mathematical						
Musical						
Bodily-Kinesthetic						
Spatial						
Interpersonal						
Intrapersonal						
Naturalist						

Career Skills (page 98)	
Most Developed Skills:	
Skills to Develop:	

Enterprise Strengths (page 100)	5	10	15	20
Opportunity Awareness				
Idea Generation				
Risk Assessment				
Information Analysis				
Resource Management				
Problem Solving				

	25	50	75	100
Entrepreneur Score (page 103):				

Learning Styles Quiz (page 115)	6	12	18	24	30	36	42	48
Practical:								
Active:								
Reflective:								
Objective:								

Learning Strengths (page 119)	
My Learning Strengths:	
My Learning Weaknesses:	

Study Skills Questionnaire (pg 122)	15	30	45	60
Place of Study				
Organisation				
Motivation and Goal Setting				
Reading Skills				
Note Taking Skills				
Revising and Exam Preparation				
Examination Performance				

CAO Choices (page 155)	
Top Level 8:	
Top Level 6/7:	

PLC Choices (page 163)	
Top PLC Courses:	
(from Priority Grid)	

Course Investigation (page 167)	
Course Investigations completed:	

World of Work (page 170)	
Top 3 Work Satisfiers - 1:	
2:	
3:	

Top Four Career Sectors (page 178)	
Sector 1:	
Sector 2:	
Sector 3:	
Sector 4:	

Career Investigation (page 180)	
Career Investigations completed:	

Work Experience (page 182)		
Company Name:	Dates:	Career Area:

Careers Log

As you progress through your senior cycle years you will have many opportunities to consider and reconsider your career direction. Working through the **Reach⁺** programme, visiting college open days and career fairs, listening to presentations by colleges, completing work experience etc., all contribute to your growing understanding of the vast range of career possibilities available.

Logging your thoughts and considerations during this period can be a valuable exercise. Complete the form below each time you consider new possibilities or reconsider old ones. Only note options which you are seriously considering at the time!

Example:

Date:	What you did:	What you're thinking of:
16 Sept	Higher Options Careers Fair	Aeronautical engineering
21 Sept	Dreams & Ambitions exercise	Architecture, professional sports player or club manager

Date:	What you did:	What you're thinking of:

Date:	What you did:	What you're thinking of:
Date:	What you did:	What you're thinking of:

Date:	What you did:	What you're thinking of:
Date:	What you did:	What you're thinking of:

Reach⁺

Visiting Speaker

Name: _____

Organisation Name: _____

Organisation Type: _____

Date: _____

Main Points: _____

_____

_____

_____

_____

_____

_____

_____

_____

_____

_____

_____

_____

_____

_____

_____

Personal Evaluation (What I got out of it): _____

_____

_____

_____

_____

_____

_____

_____

_____

_____

_____

Visiting Speaker

Name: _____

Organisation Name: _____

Organisation Type: _____

Date: _____

Main Points: _____

_____

_____

_____

_____

_____

_____

_____

_____

_____

_____

_____

_____

_____

Personal Evaluation (What I got out of it): _____

_____

_____

_____

_____

_____

_____

_____

_____

_____

_____

Reach+

Visiting Speaker

Name: _____

Organisation Name: _____

Organisation Type: _____

Date: _____

Main Points: _____

_____

_____

_____

_____

_____

_____

_____

_____

_____

_____

_____

_____

_____

_____

Personal Evaluation (What I got out of it): _____

_____

_____

_____

_____

_____

_____

_____

_____

_____

_____

_____

Notes